Presenting
Southern-inspired home plans
by Donald A. Gardner Architects, Inc.

A DESIGNS DIRECT PUBLISHING BOOK

Presented by

Donald A. Gardner Architects, Inc.
150 Executive Center Drive, Suite 215
Greenville, SC 29615

Donald A. Gardner — CEO and Publisher
Angela Santerini — President
Dominic Foley — Publisher
Kathleen Nalley — Editor
Sherrill Robertson-Bland — Graphic Artist
Paula Powers — Writer

Contributing Illustrators
Greg Havens
Barry Nathan
Architectural Art

Contributing Photographers
Matthew Scott Photographer, Inc.
Photographic Solutions
Riley & Riley Photography, Inc.
Stephen Stinson Photography
Windward Photography

Cover photo by Riley & Riley Photography, Inc.
Printed by Toppan Printing Co., Hong Kong

First Printing, January 2005

10 9 8 7 6 5 4 3 2 1

Table of Contents

Southern Soul

All Things Southern • The Designs of Donald A. Gardner Architects, Inc.

Long before European settlers, the Cherokees believed the South had a pulse — a movement or rhythm that identified with the soul. From the South came Gospel, Blues and Bluegrass; Jazz, Country and Rock-n-Roll; and Zydeco, Ragtime and Roots music. The South created Cakewalks, Clogging and the Charleston, as well as the Shag, the Virginia Reel and the Twist. From doors at the end of back alleys to churches at the end of the byways, you're likely to find a group of people clapping their hands, keeping time with the pulse of the South — the common denominator in such a culturally diverse region.

Tradition, superstition and religion permeate the South, making it a land of enchantment and stories. The South experienced its own Dark Age, Renaissance and Enlightenment, and every period has left its mark in the songs and literature of the region. But it is the area's architecture that separates history from lore. Architecture doesn't just tell you of the things that used to be — it shows you.

One of the greatest documentors of Southern architecture is the individual home. A home reflects the personalities of its family, community and time. It shelters and stores both memories and mementos. So quite simply, a home captures the soul — enveloping and nurturing the people that make up the charm and grace of the South.

Southern Chic

Southern Chic is as diverse as the region. It is a combination of the polished and faded, the mint and imperfect, the inexpensive and costly. While heavily rooted in the past, it's open to the new.

Southern Chic is personal, yet is shared — like a flower clipping from a friend's garden. It is taking objects and adapting them to your own wants or needs, whether you use them as intended or give them a whole new life or task.

Southern Chic incorporates the familiar and exotic, borrowing three basic influences from the past: customs and cultures of its settlers; materials and resources available in its own region; and a fascination for what its port cities brought to market. With faux finishes that evoke the Old World, cotton from its own fields and collectibles from around the globe, consider how much is still true today.

Southern Chic is casual elegance. It's not only an appreciation of the finer things — it's turning them into experiences that can be enjoyed every day. It's taking a common element and giving it a place of honor.

Whether you were born in the South, relocated to the South or want to take a little of the South with you on your journey, Southern Chic style welcomes you. Embrace it and your home is bound to be both beautiful and comfortable. It will reflect your personality, give you a sense of history, and add a touch of charm to your life!

Southern Soul and Southern Chic are at their best when incorporated into a home. The purpose of this book is to provide you with a collection of home plans that let the essence of both live to the fullest. Whether you're looking for a coastal or mountain home, or perhaps a home that enhances a city lot or pristine stretch  of country, these pages are filled with homes inspired by the South. Here is what you will discover in this unique and inspiring portfolio...

We Gather Together encourages Southern hospitality with innovative kitchens and open common areas.

There Is a Place exhibits Southern charm with architecturally detailed and authentic exteriors.

Just Outside the Door takes advantage of the Southern setting, expanding living and entertaining space to the great outdoors.

Lay My Burdens Down unveils Southern comfort with master suites and private areas designed as retreats from everyday life.

Welcome to our homes, and please don't be offended if we call you ma'am or sir. It's just the Southern way.

Southern Introductions

We Gather Together

*A*nyone who visits the South discovers Southern hospitality. It's so innate in the culture that Southerners often don't notice it being there, but they definitely know when it isn't.

It's only natural that a Southern home should be as accommodating as possible — to family, friends or friends-to-be, and to groups large or small. That's why the homes in this section demonstrate hospitality in both obvious and subtle ways. Here you will find innovative kitchens and gathering areas that feature step-saving designs, space for the latest amenities, room for plenty of cooks and, of course, company. After all, entertaining is what the South is all about.

(Opposite page) Tile flooring, an exquisite fireplace and French doors enhance the formal living room.

(This page) Crown molding and hardwood floors create an elegant dining experience.

grace in ABUNDANCE

This custom-designed estate home elegantly combines stone and stucco, arched windows and stunning exterior details under its formidable hip roof. The two-story foyer is impressive with its grand staircase, tray ceiling and overlooking balcony. Equally remarkable is the generous living room with fireplace and coffered two-story ceiling. The kitchen, breakfast bay and family room with fireplace are all open to one another for a comfortable, casual atmosphere. The first-floor master suite indulges with numerous closets, a dressing area and a fabulous bath. Upstairs, four more bedrooms are topped by tray ceilings; three have walk-in closets; two have private baths. The three-car garage boasts additional storage and a bonus room above.

My family has lived in this region for eleven generations, and it's exciting to know five generations will be in my home during the holidays.

I just hope our family-tree tapestry is completed in time for everyone to see it. We've reserved space for it in the two-story living room.

(Left) A center island and ample counter space allow room for more than one cook.

(Right) A curved balcony overlooks the foyer.

(Above) The casual family room invites friends and family to gather together.

SECOND FLOOR

Rear Rendering

Photographed home may have been modified from
the original construction documents.

Wedgewood

Plan ATSDG01-806

- Total Living: 5158 s.f.
- First Floor: 3520 s.f.
- Second Floor: 1638 s.f.
- Bonus Room: 411 s.f.
- 5 Bedrooms, 4 1/2 Baths
- Width: 96'6"
- Depth: 72'0"
- Crawlspace Foundation
- Price Category I

1-800-388-7580
www.allthingssouthern.com

FIRST FLOOR

genteel

EMBRACE

We Gather Together • The Designs of Donald A. Gardner Architects, Inc.

(Opposite Page) An open floor plan creates a natural traffic flow.

(This Page) Cedar shake, siding and brick fashion a home with stunning curb appeal.

© 1999 Donald A. Gardner, Inc.

With its stunning combination of hip roof and bold, front facing gables, this traditional brick-and-siding home is extraordinarily elegant. Tray and vaulted ceilings increase the feeling of spaciousness in key rooms, while the home's openness and easy flow create a comfortable, casual atmosphere. Nine-foot ceilings on the first floor expand rooms vertically. The master suite is conveniently located on the first floor and includes a generous bath and walk-in closet. The first-floor study/bedroom is a versatile space with a nearby full bath. Upstairs, two bedrooms share a hall bath and access to the large bonus room, which can be used as a children's retreat or a home office.

We both grew up on country sunshine, and when we moved to the city, we wanted to bring a little with us.

So we chose a vibrant yellow for the formal dining room, and all our friends say it's the most cheerful room to be in.

(Left) This modified tray ceiling features an octagonal design.

(Below Left) The angled counter allows room for conversation and quick meals.

(Below Right) Warm honey floors correlate with the striking staircase.

We Gather Together • The Designs of Donald A. Gardner Architects, Inc.

FIRST FLOOR

DECK

GREAT RM.
16-8 x 17-10
(vaulted ceiling)

fireplace

BRKFST.
11-4 x 9-0

MASTER
BED RM.
15-8 x 13-4

walk-in
closet

lin.

master bath

bath

UTIL.
7-10 x 6-8

w d

KIT.
11-4 x 12-8

up

cl

cl

STUDY/
BED RM.
11-0 x 12-0

FOYER
5-4 x
12-0

DINING
11-4 x 12-0

GARAGE
22-4 x 21-4

storage

PORCH

Rear Rendering

SECOND FLOOR

great room
below

BED RM.
11-0 x 12-0

cl

bath

cl

down

walk-in
closet

BED RM.
11-0 x 13-10
(vaulted ceiling)

foyer
below

BONUS RM.
15-4 x 21-4

Photographed home may have been modified from
the original construction documents.

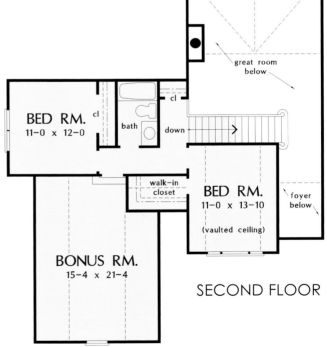

Wyndham

Plan ATSDG01-793

- Total Living: 2163 s.f.
- First Floor: 1668 s.f.
- Second Floor: 495 s.f.
- Bonus Room: 327 s.f.
- 4 Bedrooms, 3 Baths
- Width: 52'7"
- Depth: 50'11"
- Crawlspace Foundation
- Price Category C

1-800-388-7580
www.allthingssouthern.com

Modified from the plan, a ladder transom enhances visual space in the dining room.

Timeless COMFORT

This three-bedroom Craftsman home packs a lot of style into its slim façade, designed to fit narrow lots. A tray ceiling tops the formal dining room, while the kitchen features an efficient design and is open to the great room with cathedral ceiling, fireplace, built-in shelves and back-porch access. A nearby staircase leads to a generous bonus room. The master suite is located at the rear of the home and enjoys a space-enhancing cathedral ceiling, back-porch access, his-and-her walk-in closets and a private bath with garden tub and separate shower. The utility room is conveniently located in close proximity to the home's three bedrooms.

Each year I work for a theatre during Spoleto, and I have the opportunity to meet wonderful artists and performers from around the world. We usually throw a large "going away" party for the cast and crew at my house. It's amazing how attached you can get to people in such a short time.

(Left) This cozy front porch invites guests to stay a while.

Rear Rendering

© 1999 Donald A. Gardner, Inc.

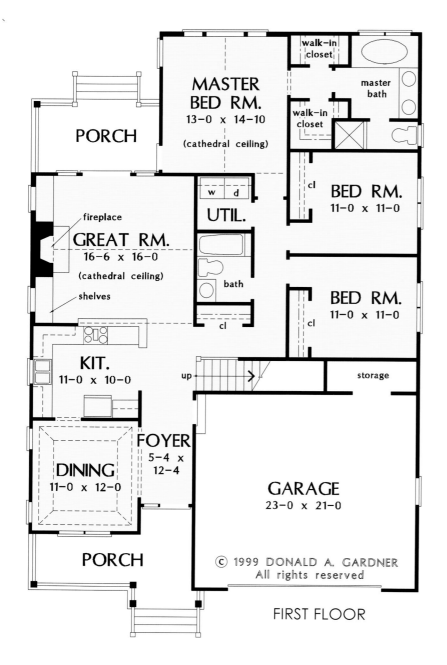

PORCH

MASTER BED RM.
13-0 x 14-10
(cathedral ceiling)

walk-in closet

master bath

walk-in closet

w   d

UTIL.

cl

BED RM.
11-0 x 11-0

fireplace

GREAT RM.
16-6 x 16-0
(cathedral ceiling)

shelves

bath

cl

BED RM.
11-0 x 11-0

cl

KIT.
11-0 x 10-0

up

storage

FOYER
5-4 x 12-4

DINING
11-0 x 12-0

GARAGE
23-0 x 21-0

PORCH

FIRST FLOOR

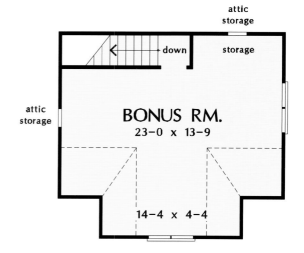

attic storage

down

storage

attic storage

BONUS RM.
23-0 x 13-9

14-4 x 4-4

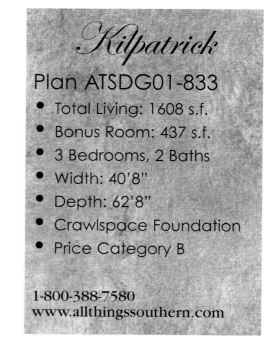

Kilpatrick

Plan ATSDG01-833

- Total Living: 1608 s.f.
- Bonus Room: 437 s.f.
- 3 Bedrooms, 2 Baths
- Width: 40'8"
- Depth: 62'8"
- Crawlspace Foundation
- Price Category B

1-800-388-7580
www.allthingssouthern.com

© 1999 Donald A. Gardner, Inc.

(Above) Gables and decorative wood brackets lend a cottage feel to this narrow-lot home.

(Left) The bonus room can function as a family room/guest suite, as a playroom for kids or as a home office for working adults.

Photographed home may have been modified from the original construction documents.

Savoir Faire

This four-bedroom Traditional makes a grand impression with multiple front-facing gables, elegant arched windows and a barrel-vaulted entry with stately columns. The foyer is enhanced by a graceful cathedral ceiling, fulfilling the promise of grandeur made by the home's exterior. Columns add definition to the casually elegant, open dining room, while the great room's spaciousness is augmented by another cathedral ceiling. The kitchen is more than generous, featuring a center work island, pantry and breakfast counter, and the sunny breakfast bay is topped by a delightful, octagonal tray ceiling. Each of the home's four bedrooms enjoys a special ceiling treatment, as does the master bath. A lovely picture window with circletop accents the versatile study/bedroom, and both bedrooms upstairs boast walk-in closets. The sunken bonus room offers generous flexibility.

Scratches in furniture or a chip in a plate helps define the history of those pieces. That's why I don't think anything is too good to use, and I'm not afraid to enjoy my good china on a regular basis. It makes guests feel special, and that's what Southern hospitality is all about.

Windows bathe the great room in natural light, creating a warm and pleasing atmosphere.

Complimentary jewel tones give the dining room
a casual elegance.

Stairs lead from the kitchen (with convenient workspace) to
a sunken bonus room upstairs.

The gracious master bath features ample storage space
and a garden tub.

Warm colors and a tray ceiling give the master suite
a comfortable ambiance.

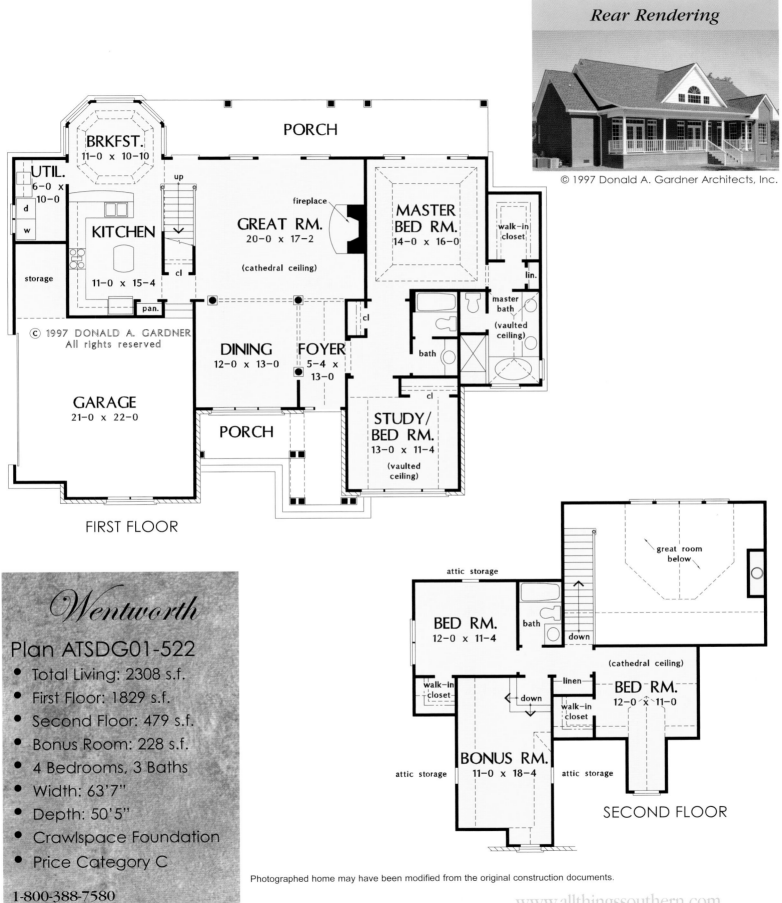

Rear Rendering

© 1997 Donald A. Gardner Architects, Inc.

PORCH

BRKFST.
11-0 x 10-10

UTIL.
6-0 x
10-0

KITCHEN
11-0 x 15-4

storage

pan.

up

cl

GREAT RM.
20-0 x 17-2
(cathedral ceiling)

fireplace

MASTER
BED RM.
14-0 x 16-0

walk-in
closet

lin.

master
bath
(vaulted
ceiling)

bath

cl

DINING
12-0 x 13-0

FOYER
5-4 x
13-0

STUDY/
BED RM.
13-0 x 11-4
(vaulted
ceiling)

cl

GARAGE
21-0 x 22-0

PORCH

FIRST FLOOR

attic storage

great room
below

BED RM.
12-0 x 11-4

bath

down

walk-in
closet

linen

down

walk-in
closet

(cathedral ceiling)

BED RM.
12-0 x 11-0

BONUS RM.
11-0 x 18-4

attic storage

attic storage

SECOND FLOOR

Wentworth

Plan ATSDG01-522

- Total Living: 2308 s.f.
- First Floor: 1829 s.f.
- Second Floor: 479 s.f.
- Bonus Room: 228 s.f.
- 4 Bedrooms, 3 Baths
- Width: 63'7"
- Depth: 50'5"
- Crawlspace Foundation
- Price Category C

1-800-388-7580
www.allthingssouthern.com

Photographed home may have been modified from the original construction documents.

SOLID *Elegance*

Restrained elegance inside and out characterizes this stunning executive home with a dynamic open floor plan. One dramatic room reveals another, beginning in the central foyer with a clerestory window. Elegant columns separate the large great room with cathedral ceiling from the smart, angled kitchen with skylit breakfast area. The great room accesses the covered, skylit rear porch and deck beyond.

Tucked away for privacy, the master suite is a grand getaway. Homeowners will pamper themselves in the well-appointed bath with corner whirlpool tub, separate shower and double-bowl vanity. The front bedroom can also be used as a study, while a bonus room over the garage adds even more flexibility. Ample storage space in the garage helps keep home and garden tidy.

Port cities offer a glimpse into other cultures, and may even be influenced by them, yet they maintain their own distinct character. My wife and I wanted our home to absorb what our city had to offer, so we went down to the docks with a group of friends and purchased items straight off the boat.

(Opposite Page) A Traditional brick exterior combined with a popular courtyard garage gives this home tremendous curb appeal.

(This Page) Heavy crown molding and generous windows add a sophisticated touch to the great room.

This sparkling white kitchen incorporates a natural traffic flow and step-saving design.

The spacious master retreat creates a private haven for the homeowner.

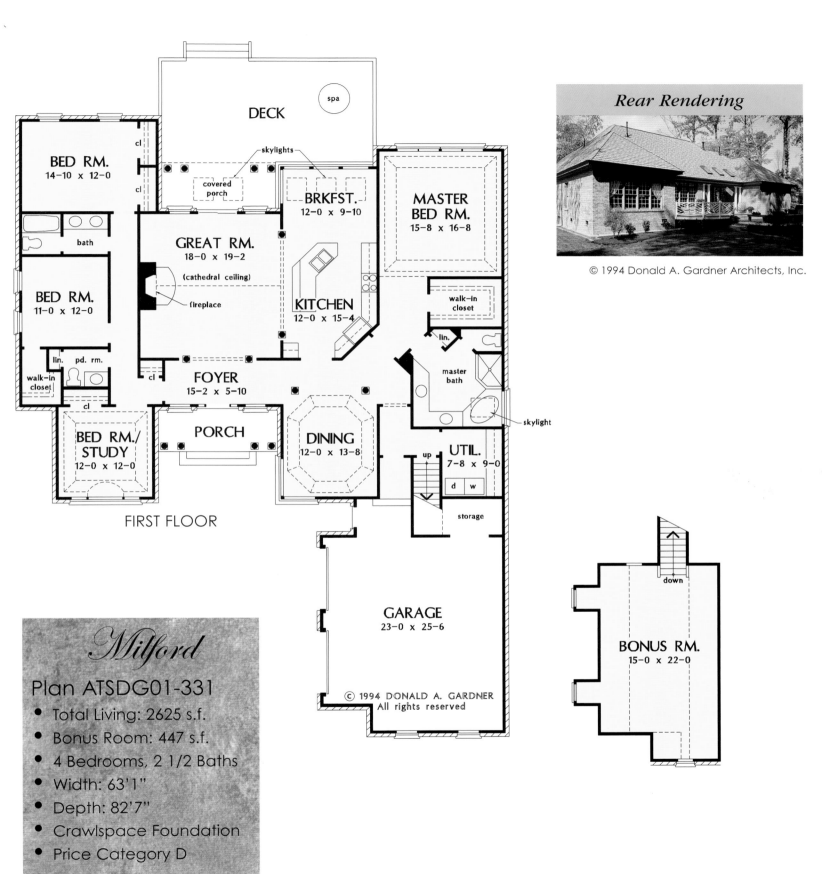

DECK

spa

BED RM.
14-10 x 12-0

cl

cl

skylights

covered
porch

BRKFST.
12-0 x 9-10

MASTER
BED RM.
15-8 x 16-8

bath

GREAT RM.
18-0 x 19-2

(cathedral ceiling)

fireplace

KITCHEN
12-0 x 15-4

walk-in
closet

BED RM.
11-0 x 12-0

lin.

lin.

master
bath

walk-in
closet

pd. rm.

walk-in
closet

cl

FOYER
15-2 x 5-10

cl

skylight

BED RM./
STUDY
12-0 x 12-0

PORCH

DINING
12-0 x 13-8

UTIL.
7-8 x 9-0

up

d   w

FIRST FLOOR

storage

GARAGE
23-0 x 25-6

© 1994 DONALD A. GARDNER
All rights reserved

Rear Rendering

© 1994 Donald A. Gardner Architects, Inc.

down

BONUS RM.
15-0 x 22-0

Milford

Plan ATSDG01-331

- Total Living: 2625 s.f.
- Bonus Room: 447 s.f.
- 4 Bedrooms, 2 1/2 Baths
- Width: 63'1"
- Depth: 82'7"
- Crawlspace Foundation
- Price Category D

1-800-388-7580
www.allthingssouthern.com

Photographed home may have been modified from the original construction documents.

Refreshing
COTTAGE REVIVAL

This Craftsman cottage combines stone, siding and cedar shake to create striking curb appeal. The interior features an open floor plan with high ceilings, columns and bay windows to visually expand space. Built-in cabinetry, a fireplace and a kitchen pass-thru both highlight and add convenience to the great room. The master suite features a tray ceiling in the bedroom and a bath with garden tub, separate shower, dual vanities and a walk-in closet. On the opposite side of the home, an additional bedroom could be used as a second master suite, and above the garage, a bonus room provides ample storage and room to grow. The bedroom/study creates a perfect library or home office.

We don't need a special occasion to have friends over for a family-style dinner with all the fixings. Sometimes we prepare it all here, and sometimes everyone will bring their favorite dish. The important thing is the fellowship and, of course, the celebration of Southern cuisine ~ desserts included!

(Opposite Page) Siding, stone and cedar shake capture quaint sophistication.

(This Page) This kitchen opens to the dining room and services the great room through a pass-thru.

(Above) A giant bay opens up the seating area in the great room, making the room function at maximum capacity.

(Bottom Right) A rear deck, accented by the curves of the home's rear, offers room for relaxation and entertainment.

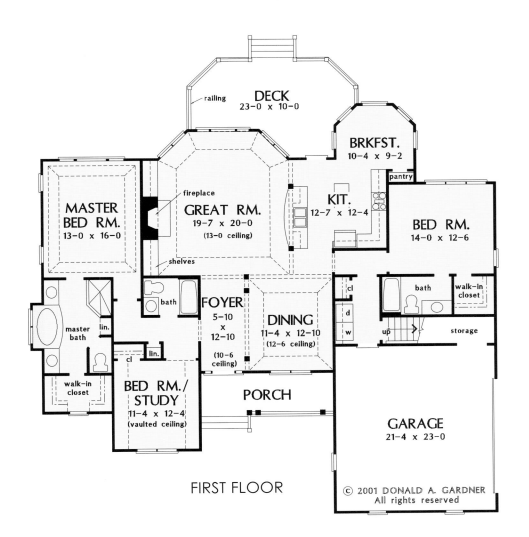

DECK
23-0 x 10-0

railing

BRKFST.
10-4 x 9-2

pantry

fireplace

MASTER
BED RM.
13-0 x 16-0

GREAT RM.
19-7 x 20-0
(13-0 ceiling)

KIT.
12-7 x 12-4

BED RM.
14-0 x 12-6

shelves

cl

bath

walk-in
closet

master
bath

lin.

bath

FOYER
5-10
x
12-10

(10-6
ceiling)

DINING
11-4 x 12-10
(12-6 ceiling)

d

w

up

storage

lin.

cl

walk-in
closet

BED RM./
STUDY
11-4 x 12-4
(vaulted ceiling)

PORCH

GARAGE
21-4 x 23-0

FIRST FLOOR

7-10 x 4-2

down

attic
storage

attic
storage

BONUS RM.
13-4 x 18-10

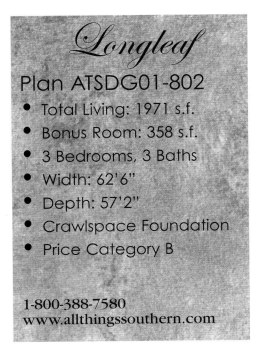

Longleaf

Plan ATSDG01-802

- Total Living: 1971 s.f.
- Bonus Room: 358 s.f.
- 3 Bedrooms, 3 Baths
- Width: 62'6"
- Depth: 57'2"
- Crawlspace Foundation
- Price Category B

1-800-388-7580
www.allthingssouthern.com

Photographed home may have been modified
from the original construction documents.

ROOM *for* ALL

A stunning center dormer with arched window embellishes the exterior of this Craftsman-style home with walkout basement. The dormer's arched window allows light into the foyer with built-in niche. The second floor's hall is a balcony that overlooks both foyer and great room. A generous back porch extends the great room, which features an impressive vaulted ceiling and fireplace, while a tray ceiling adorns the formal dining room. The master bedroom, boasting a tray ceiling as well, enjoys back-porch access, a built-in cabinet, generous walk-in closet and private bath. Two more bedrooms are located upstairs, while a fourth can be found in the basement along with a family room. Note the huge bonus room on the second level and the generous storage space in the three-car garage.

We love when the children and grandchildren come to visit, so we chose a house that had two upstairs bedrooms and a versatile bedroom/study in the basement level. The grandkids play each other in checkers to see who gets to sleep next to the family room, but they both usually fall asleep downstairs anyway.

(Opposite Page) Perfect for mountain living, this home exudes Craftsman character.

(This Page) A clerestory window, transoms and French doors usher natural light into the great room.

The family room provides a cozy retreat.

The Traditionally styled dining room is bathed in natural light.

The island cooktop provides workspace and storage.

Four-season enjoyment can be found on the modified screen porch.

PORCH

MASTER
BED RM.
14-0 x 16-0

GREAT RM.
21-0 x 15-10

(cathedral ceiling)

fireplace

balcony above

DINING
12-0 x 15-0

SCREEN
PORCH
9-4 x 9-0

KIT.

BRKFST.
10-0 x 10-0

8-8 x 13-2

walk-in
closet

master bath

lin.

cl

FOYER
6-4 x
7-4

up   down

UTIL.
8-4 x 5-8

d   w

sto.

cl

sto.

pd. rm.

PORCH

FIRST FLOOR

GARAGE
22-0 x 34-0

© 1999 DONALD A. GARDNER
All rights reserved

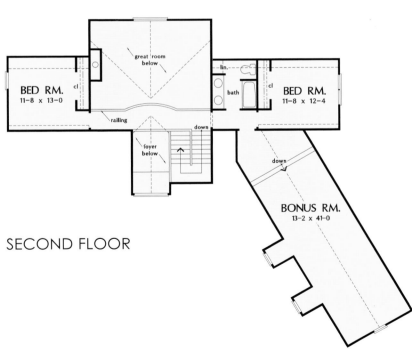
PATIO

UNFINISHED
STORAGE/
MECHANICAL
13-4 x 15-6

fireplace

FAMILY RM.
17-10 x 15-4

wet bar

cl

BED RM./
STUDY
12-2 x 10-0

bath

up   sto.

BASEMENT FLOOR

BED RM.
11-8 x 13-0

cl

great room
below

railing

lin.

bath

cl

BED RM.
11-8 x 12-4

foyer
below

down

down

BONUS RM.
13-2 x 41-0

SECOND FLOOR

Peekskill

Plan ATSDG01-780

- Total Living: 2953 s.f.
- First Floor: 1662 s.f.
- Second Floor: 585 s.f.
- Basement Floor: 706 s.f.
- Bonus Room: 575 s.f.
- 4 Bedrooms, 3 1/2 Baths
- Width: 81'4"
- Depth: 68'8"
- Hillside Walkout Foundation
- Price Category D

1-800-388-7580
www.allthingssouthern.com

Photographed home may have been modified from the original construction documents.

we gather together
Donald A. Gardner Architects, Inc.

Violet

*O*ne of my favorite wedding presents was an album full of my family's recipes. It's well-used and proudly displayed in the kitchen. Friends always request the jambalaya.

Plan ATSDG01-1016

- Total Living: 1660 s.f.
- Bonus Room: 374 s.f.
- 3 Bedrooms, 2 Baths
- Width: 65'4"
- Depth: 48'8"
- Crawlspace Foundation
- Price Category B

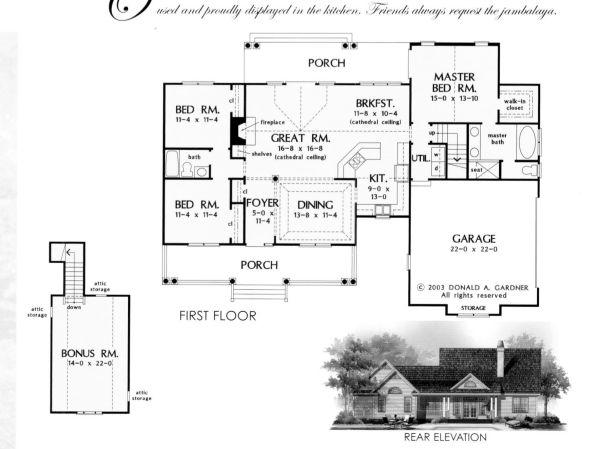

FIRST FLOOR

PORCH

BED RM.
11-4 x 11-4

GREAT RM.
16-8 x 16-8
(cathedral ceiling)

fireplace

shelves

bath

BED RM.
11-4 x 11-4

FOYER
5-0 x 11-4

DINING
13-8 x 11-4

BRKFST.
11-8 x 10-4
(cathedral ceiling)

KIT.
9-0 x 13-0

UTIL.

up

MASTER BED RM.
15-0 x 13-10

walk-in closet

master bath

seat

PORCH

GARAGE
22-0 x 22-0

STORAGE

BONUS RM.
14-0 x 22-0

attic storage

down

attic storage

attic storage

REAR ELEVATION

1-800-388-7580
www.allthingssouthern.com

When we purchased land in the Smoky Mountains, we envisioned a rustic cabin with two good-sized porches for observing nature and relaxing with family and friends.

Meredith

Plan ATSDG01-355

- Total Living: 1694 s.f.
- First Floor: 1100 s.f.
- Second Floor: 594 s.f.
- 3 Bedrooms, 2 Baths
- Width: 36'8"
- Depth: 45'0"
- Crawlspace Foundation
- Price Category B

SECOND FLOOR

LOFT/STUDY
12-0 x 14-0

master bath

walk-in closet

MASTER BED RM.
12-0 x 14-0

railing

down

great room below

attic storage

FIRST FLOOR

w d cl

UTILITY
8-4 x 7-8

PORCH

KIT.
8-0 x 11-4

bath

BED RM.
12-0 x 10-0

DINING
10-4 x 11-2

cl

lin.

cl

balcony above

cl

GREAT RM.
17-4 x 17-0

fireplace

up

BED RM.
12-0 x 13-4

PORCH

REAR ELEVATION

© 1995 Donald A. Gardner Architects, Inc.

Reidville

*W*e're located right next to a historic district, and many visitors assume our house is a part of it. Our home really does blend with our much older neighbors.

Plan ATSDG01-424

- Total Living: 1792 s.f.
- First Floor: 959 s.f.
- Second Floor: 833 s.f.
- Bonus Room: 344 s.f.
- 3 Bedrooms, 2 1/2 Baths
- Width: 52'6"
- Depth: 42'8"
- Crawlspace Foundation
- Price Category B

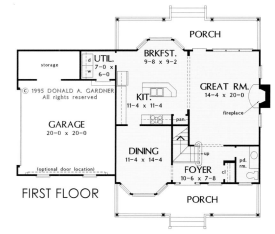

FIRST FLOOR

SECOND FLOOR

REAR ELEVATION

When we returned home from the hospital, my mother, grandmother and great-grandmother came over to welcome our new baby.

Ringgold

Plan ATSDG01-1056

- Total Living: 1886 s.f.
- Bonus Room: 588 s.f.
- 3 Bedrooms, 2 Baths
- Width: 51'6"
- Depth: 65'8"
- Crawlspace Foundation
- Price Category B

LOFT/STUDY
8-6 x 22-8

attic storage

attic storage

BONUS RM.
14-0 x 22-0

down

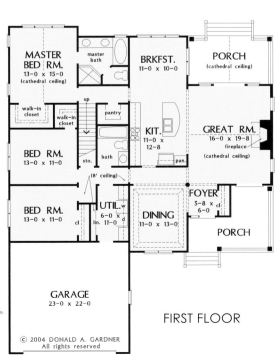

MASTER BED RM.
13-0 x 15-0
(cathedral ceiling)

master bath

BRKFST.
11-0 x 10-0

PORCH
(cathedral ceiling)

walk-in closet

walk-in closet

pantry

up

KIT.
11-0 x 12-8

GREAT RM.
16-0 x 19-8
fireplace
(cathedral ceiling)

BED RM.
13-0 x 11-0

sto.

bath

pan.

BED RM.
13-0 x 11-0

UTIL.
6-0 x 11-0

(8' ceiling)

DINING
11-0 x 13-0

FOYER
5-8 x 6-0

PORCH

lin.

GARAGE
23-0 x 22-0

FIRST FLOOR

REAR ELEVATION

1-800-388-7580
www.allthingssouthern.com

43

Giovanni

The house is filled with Little League players nearly every Saturday during season. After each game, we grill hot dogs and burgers, while recapping game highlights.

Plan ATSDG01-1059

- Total Living: 1921 s.f.
- Bonus Room: 449 s.f.
- 3 Bedrooms, 2 Baths
- Width: 62'6"
- Depth: 49'8"
- Crawlspace Foundation
- Price Category B

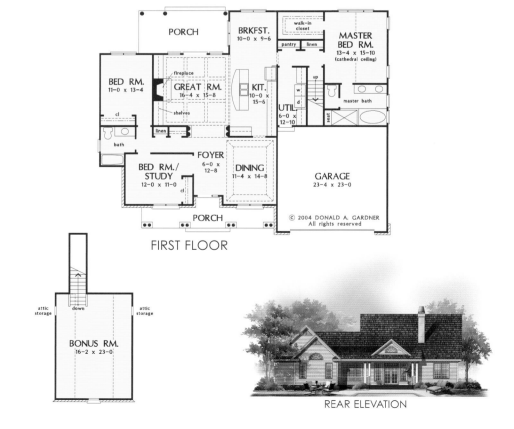

FIRST FLOOR

BONUS RM.
16-2 x 23-0

REAR ELEVATION

*O*ur dining room table is a salvaged door from an old cotton mill.
It sits twelve very comfortably and lends a nostalgic sentiment to the décor.

Applemoor

Plan ATSDG01-970

- Total Living: 1952 s.f.
- Bonus Room: 339 s.f.
- 4 Bedrooms, 3 Baths
- Width: 50'0"
- Depth: 60'0"
- Crawlspace Foundation
- Price Category B

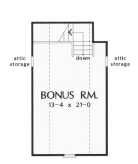

BONUS RM.
13-4 x 21-0

attic storage — down — attic storage

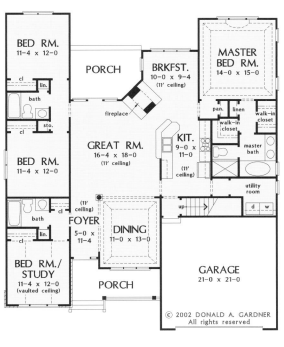

FIRST FLOOR

REAR ELEVATION

1-800-388-7580
www.allthingssouthern.com

45

we gather together
Donald A. Gardner Architects, Inc.

Taylor

My friends and I never miss the Azalea Festival in the summer or the Pumpkin Festival in the fall. My kitchen sets the stage for pre-festival parties.

Plan ATSDG01-427

- Total Living: 1963 s.f.
- First Floor: 1456 s.f.
- Second Floor: 507 s.f.
- Bonus Room: 380 s.f.
- 3 Bedrooms, 2 1/2 Baths
- Width: 78'4"
- Depth: 51'4"
- Crawlspace Foundation
- Price Category B

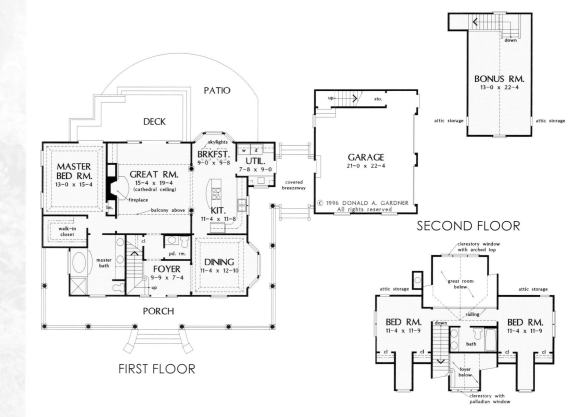

BONUS RM.
13-0 x 22-4

attic storage   attic storage

SECOND FLOOR

FIRST FLOOR

PATIO

DECK

MASTER BED RM.
13-0 x 15-4

GREAT RM.
15-4 x 19-4
(cathedral ceiling)
fireplace

balcony above

walk-in closet

master bath

lin.

FOYER
9-9 x 7-4

up

PORCH

BRKFST.
9-0 x 9-8

skylights

UTIL.
7-8 x 9-0

w d

KIT.
11-4 x 11-8

cl

pd. rm.

DINING
11-4 x 12-10

covered breezeway

up   sto.

GARAGE
21-0 x 22-4

© 1996 DONALD A. GARDNER
All rights reserved

clerestory window with arched top

great room below

attic storage   attic storage

railing

BED RM.
11-4 x 11-9

down

bath

BED RM.
11-4 x 11-9

cl   cl   cl   cl

foyer below

clerestory with palladian window

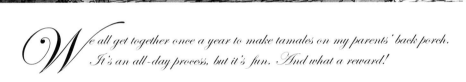

We all get together once a year to make tamales on my parents' back porch. It's an all-day process, but it's fun. And what a reward!

Hanover

Plan ATSDG01-489

- Total Living: 2023 s.f.
- First Floor: 1489 s.f.
- Second Floor: 534 s.f.
- Bonus Room: 393 s.f.
- 3 Bedrooms, 2 1/2 Baths
- Width: 59'4"
- Depth: 58'7"
- Crawlspace Foundation
- Price Category C

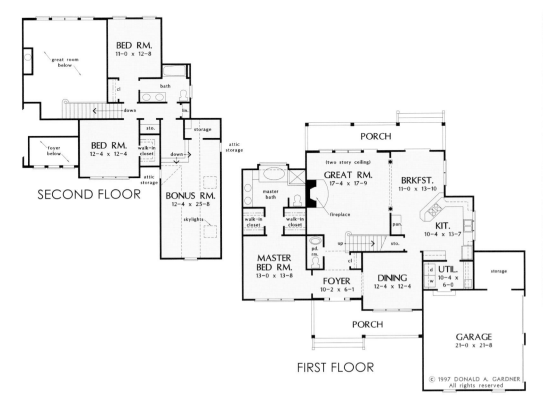

SECOND FLOOR

FIRST FLOOR

we gather together

Donald A. Gardner Architects, Inc.

Buckhead

The new silk drapes came in one week before we were to host the anniversary party. I was so happy the great room was completed in time.

Plan ATSDG01-707

- Total Living: 2024 s.f.
- Bonus Room: 423 s.f.
- 3 Bedrooms, 2 1/2 Baths
- Width: 62'3"
- Depth: 74'9"
- Crawlspace Foundation
- Price Category C

SCREEN PORCH
15-6 x 14-0

DECK

BRKFST.
10-4 x 9-0

GREAT RM.
19-0 x 16-0

MASTER BED RM.
16-4 x 13-4

fireplace

(cathedral ceiling)

KIT.
10-4 x 12-0

BED RM./STUDY
12-4 x 12-10

walk-in closet

walk-in closet

bath

DINING
12-0 x 14-0

FOYER
6-0 x 11-10

pd. rm.

master bath

up

UTIL.
6-4 x 8-10

BED RM.
12-4 x 11-0

walk-in closet

PORCH

FIRST FLOOR

GARAGE
22-8 x 23-0

attic storage

down

BONUS RM.
16-4 x 23-0

REAR ELEVATION

1-800-388-7580
www.allthingssouthern.com

The whole community still participates in our church socials and town dances. Several couples meet at our house, and we go to the events together.

Calhoun

Plan ATSDG01-392

- Total Living: 2192 s.f.
- Bonus Room: 390 s.f.
- 4 Bedrooms, 2 1/2 Baths
- Width: 74'10"
- Depth: 55'8"
- Crawlspace Foundation
- Price Category C

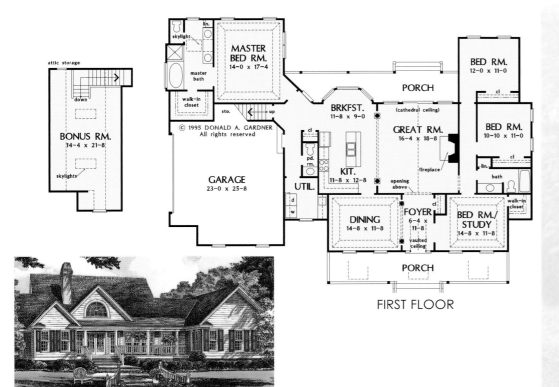

attic storage

BONUS RM.
14-4 x 21-8

skylights

down

MASTER BED RM.
14-0 x 17-4

master bath

walk-in closet

skylight

lin.

© 1995 DONALD A. GARDNER
All rights reserved

GARAGE
23-0 x 25-8

UTIL.

sto.

up

BRKFST.
11-8 x 9-0

KIT.
11-8 x 12-8

pd. rm.

DINING
14-8 x 11-8

vaulted ceiling

FOYER
6-4 x 11-8

(cathedral ceiling)

GREAT RM.
16-4 x 18-8

fireplace

opening above

PORCH

BED RM.
12-0 x 11-0

cl

BED RM.
10-10 x 11-0

cl

lin.

bath

walk-in closet

BED RM./ STUDY
14-8 x 11-8

PORCH

FIRST FLOOR

REAR ELEVATION

we gather together
Donald A. Gardner Architects, Inc.

Belhaven

Featuring red-clay brick ~ the man-made "jewel" of the South ~ brick homes have long been a tradition in my family. They couldn't wait to see mine built.

Plan ATSDG01-516

- Total Living: 2250 s.f.
- First Floor: 1644 s.f.
- Second Floor: 606 s.f.
- Bonus Room: 548 s.f.
- 3 Bedrooms, 2 1/2 Baths
- Width: 61'7"
- Depth: 67'4"
- Crawlspace Foundation
- Price Category C

FIRST FLOOR

SCREEN PORCH 12-0 x 11-0
PORCH
GREAT RM. 17-4 x 17-9 (two story ceiling) fireplace
BRKFST. 12-0 x 11-0
master bath
walk-in closet
walk-in closet
KITCHEN 12-4 x 13-11
pan.
MASTER BED RM. 13-0 x 14-0
FOYER 11-4 x 6-5 (two story ceiling)
pd. rm.
up cl
DINING 12-4 x 12-8
up
UTILITY 10-6 x 6-10
w d
storage
PORCH
GARAGE 22-4 x 21-8

SECOND FLOOR

great room below
BED RM. 12-0 x 12-8
walk-in closet
bath
bath
linen
foyer below
BED RM. 12-4 x 12-8
walk-in closet
down
cl
storage
skylights
BONUS RM. 15-6 x 21-8

1-800-388-7580
www.allthingssouthern.com

© 2004 Donald A. Gardner, Inc.

In preparation for the Strawberry Festival, my wife lined our counters with a dozen home-baked pies, while the kids and I made ice cream on the back porch.

Vissage

SECOND FLOOR

REAR ELEVATION

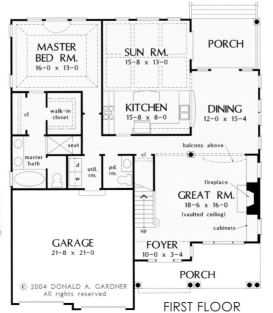

FIRST FLOOR

Plan ATSDG01-1063

- Total Living: 2351 s.f.
- First Floor: 1575 s.f.
- Second Floor: 776 s.f.
- Bonus Room: 394 s.f.
- 3 Bedrooms, 2 1/2 Baths
- Width: 45'0"
- Depth: 54'0"
- Crawlspace Foundation
- Price Category C

© 2002 Donald A. Gardner, Inc.

Heywood

My mother believed Southern ladies should know how to play the piano, so my sisters and I took lessons. I now teach piano in my great room.

Plan ATSDG01-991

- Total Living: 2485 s.f.
- First Floor: 1420 s.f.
- Second Floor: 1065 s.f.
- Bonus Room: 411 s.f.
- 4 Bedrooms, 3 Baths
- Width: 57'8"
- Depth: 49'0"
- Crawlspace Foundation
- Price Category C

SECOND FLOOR

FIRST FLOOR

REAR ELEVATION

*O*ur eclectic container garden is accessible from the great room's French doors and is a wonderful spot to host brunches or afternoon tea.

Petalquilt

Plan ATSDG01-1026

- Total Living: 2647 s.f.
- First Floor: 1848 s.f.
- Second Floor: 799 s.f.
- Bonus Room: 457 s.f.
- 3 Bedrooms, 3 1/2 Baths
- Width: 81'0"
- Depth: 49'8"
- Crawlspace Foundation
- Price Category D

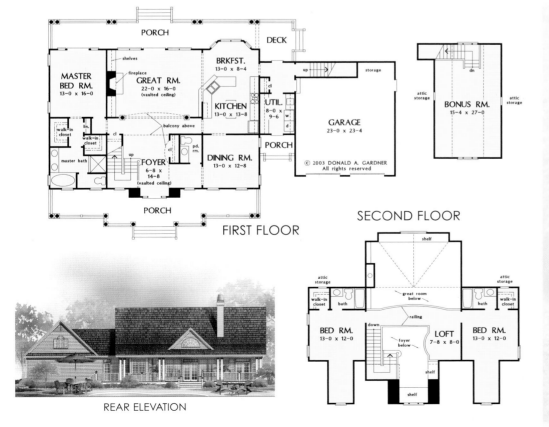

FIRST FLOOR

SECOND FLOOR

REAR ELEVATION

© 2003 Donald A. Gardner, Inc.

Colridge

Plan ATSDG01-1012

- Total Living: 2652 s.f.
- First Floor: 1732 s.f.
- Basement Floor: 920 s.f.
- 3 Bedrooms, 3 Baths
- Width: 70'6"
- Depth: 59'6"
- Hillside Walkout Foundation
- Price Category D

Our entire common space is conducive to parties large and small. The cook is always a part of the action, and guests can participate in the preparations.

BASEMENT FLOOR

FIRST FLOOR

REAR ELEVATION

Photographed home may have been modified from the original construction documents.

W̶e were hiking with friends near our house, and we found an intensely dark red leaf — the perfect color match for our dining room.

Bentonville

Plan ATSDG01-308

- Total Living: 2658 s.f.
- First Floor: 2064 s.f.
- Second Floor: 594 s.f.
- Bonus Room: 483 s.f.
- 4 Bedrooms, 3 1/2 Baths
- Width: 92'0"
- Depth: 57'8"
- Crawlspace Foundation
- Price Category D

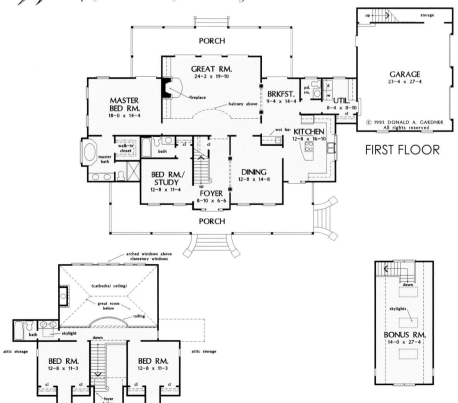

PORCH

GREAT RM.
24-2 x 19-10

fireplace

balcony above

MASTER
BED RM.
18-0 x 14-4

BRKFST.
9-4 x 14-4

pd. rm.

UTIL
8-4 x 8-10

GARAGE
23-4 x 27-4

up   storage

master bath

walk-in closet

bath

wet bar

KITCHEN
12-8 x 16-10

FIRST FLOOR

BED RM./
STUDY
12-8 x 11-3

DINING
12-8 x 14-8

FOYER
8-10 x 6-6

PORCH

arched windows above clerestory windows

(cathedral ceiling)

great room below

railing

bath   skylight

attic storage

down

attic storage

BED RM.
12-8 x 11-3

BED RM.
12-8 x 11-3

foyer below

clerestory with palladian window

SECOND FLOOR

down

skylights

BONUS RM.
14-0 x 27-4

© 2000 Donald A. Gardner, Inc.

Valencia

Reflecting a Mediterranean style, this home fits any sun-kissed state perfectly; after the promotion, we built ours in Texas.

Plan ATSDG01-907

- Total Living: 2600 s.f.
- First Floor: 1679 s.f.
- Second Floor: 921 s.f.
- 4 Bedrooms, 2 1/2 Baths
- Width: 58'0"
- Depth: 58'10"
- Crawlspace Foundation
- Price Category D

FIRST FLOOR

SECOND FLOOR

REAR ELEVATION

Our tapestry is one of our prized possessions. Hanging in our dining room, it features a large outdoor feast in the Renaissance period.

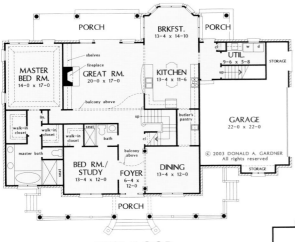

FIRST FLOOR

REAR ELEVATION

SECOND FLOOR

Fitzgerald

Plan ATSDG01-1018

- Total Living: 3196 s.f.
- First Floor: 2215 s.f.
- Second Floor: 981 s.f.
- Bonus Room: 402 s.f.
- 5 Bedrooms, 4 Baths
- Width: 71'11"
- Depth: 55'10"
- Crawlspace Foundation
- Price Category E

1-800-388-7580
www.allthingssouthern.com

57

Tuscany

Each one of our supper-club events has a different theme, and we utilize every gathering room to create the appropriate ambiance.

Plan ATSDG01-877

- Total Living: 3219 s.f.
- First Floor: 2477 s.f.
- Second Floor: 742 s.f.
- Bonus Room: 419 s.f.
- 4 Bedrooms, 4 Baths
- Width: 99'10"
- Depth: 66'2"
- Crawlspace Foundation
- Price Category E

FIRST FLOOR

SECOND FLOOR

REAR ELEVATION

we gather together
Donald A. Gardner Architects, Inc.

© 2002 Donald A. Gardner, Inc.

Full of folklore, this mountain is where we wanted our home. Our walkout overlooks the valley and accommodates a yearly costume party honoring the legends.

Laycrest

Plan ATSDG01-995

- Total Living: 3320 s.f.
- First Floor: 1720 s.f.
- Basement Floor: 1600 s.f.
- 4 Bedrooms, 3 1/2 Baths
- Width: 59'0"
- Depth: 59'4"
- Hillside Walkout Foundation
- Price Category E

FIRST FLOOR

DINING 12-0 x 15-0
PORCH
MASTER BED RM. 14-0 x 18-0
PORCH
fireplace
GREAT RM. 22-0 x 18-6 (cathedral ceiling)
KITCHEN 12-0 x 15-0
BRKFST. 9-8 x 10-0
walk-in closet
walk-in closet
railing
UTIL. 5-8 x 6-8
pantry
storage
pd. rm.
cl
FOYER 6-8 x 10-0
master bath
niche
seat
GARAGE 21-8 x 21-4
PORCH
storage

BASEMENT FLOOR

PORCH
PORCH
cl
cl
BED RM. 12-0 x 15-0
fireplace
BED RM. 13-6 x 15-0
BED RM. 11-2 x 13-8
REC. RM. 19-8 x 18-6
walk-in closet
bath
cl
cl
lin.
up
sto.
bath
BAR 8-4 x 9-0
seat
wet bar

REAR ELEVATION

There Is a Place

*W*hat is it about Southerners that creates that undeniable Southern charm? Is it the lingering smiles, slow handshakes or homegrown manners? And how is it that you can drive through so many towns and cities and see so many buildings, streets and other things that are, well, so charming? There are some people and places that put you at ease from the first moment you see them. There are people and places that make you feel good, and it's that charm that draws you to them. Whatever style you're drawn to, the homes in this section are chosen for their charming exteriors. Displaying attention to detail, they welcome you, give you a sense of place and simply make you feel good.

Captivating CURB APPEAL

Long ago, homes blended with their environments, because people used materials that were nearby. We wanted to maintain the integrity of our natural setting, so we chose materials that looked as if they came from our area.

Graceful arches contrast with high gables for a stunning exterior on this Craftsman home. Windows with decorative transoms and several French doors flood the open floor plan with natural light. Tray ceilings in the dining room and master bedroom, as well as cathedral ceilings in the bedroom/study, great room, kitchen and breakfast area, create architectural interest along with visual space. Built-ins in the great room and additional room in the garage add convenient storage. A screened porch allows for comfortable outdoor entertaining. A bonus room lies near two additional bedrooms and offers flexibility. Positioned for privacy, the master suite features access to the screened porch, dual walk-in closets and a well-appointed bath, including a private toilet, garden tub, double vanity and spacious shower.

(Opposite Page) With keystone arches, a coffered porch ceiling and arched transoms, this home incorporates architectural interest.

(This Page) This great room is as comforable as it is stylish — with gracious built-ins and unique fireplace.

(Above) Wainscoting and a tray ceiling highlight the formal dining room, which is open to the great room for a natural gathering area.

(Left) Incorporating a step-saving design, the kitchen makes routine tasks easier. Granite countertops offer both a high level of function and style.

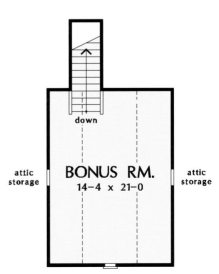

Rear Rendering

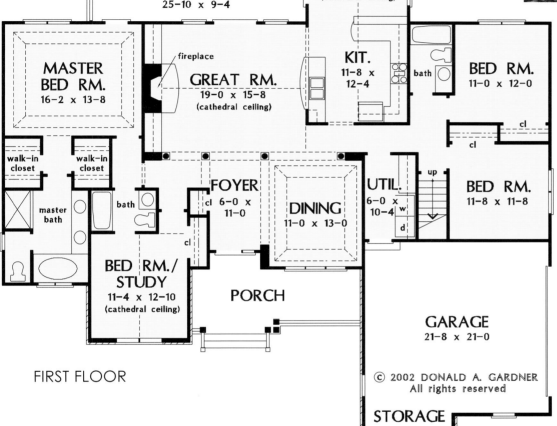

SCREEN PORCH
25-10 x 9-4

BRKFST.
11-8 x 8-10
(cathedral ceiling)

MASTER BED RM.
16-2 x 13-8

fireplace

GREAT RM.
19-0 x 15-8
(cathedral ceiling)

KIT.
11-8 x 12-4

bath

BED RM.
11-0 x 12-0

walk-in closet

walk-in closet

cl

cl

master bath

bath

FOYER
cl 6-0 x 11-0

UTIL.
6-0 x 10-4

up

w

d

BED RM.
11-8 x 11-8

DINING
11-0 x 13-0

BED RM./ STUDY
11-4 x 12-10
(cathedral ceiling)

cl

PORCH

GARAGE
21-8 x 21-0

STORAGE

FIRST FLOOR

Satchwell

Plan ATSDG01-967

- Total Living: 2097 s.f.
- Bonus Room: 352 s.f.
- 4 Bedrooms, 3 Baths
- Width: 64'10"
- Depth: 59'6"
- Crawlspace Foundation
- Price Category C

1-800-388-7580
www.allthingssouthern.com

down

attic storage

BONUS RM.
14-4 x 21-0

attic storage

© 2003 Donald A. Gardner, Inc.

modified
Beauty

On our lazy days we sit on the front porch, sip coffee and watch the children play ball in the front yard. Last week, I just knew the ball was going to crash through the clerestory window, but it didn't. It hit the cedar shake instead. I guess you never can tell with a foul ball.

(Opposite Page) Modified from the original plan, the front elevation is a mixture of cedar shake, stone and brick.

(This Page) This home calls for a formal living room and separate, more casual family room.

Using materials that combine the rugged frontier with stately elegance, this exterior has a grand, majestic façade. Four towering columns frame the dramatic barrel-vault entrance, while clerestory windows mimic the arched theme. Cedar shake, stone and siding complement a metal roof over the front porch. The two-story foyer has impressive views of the study, dining room, living room and balcony.

Cathedral ceilings top the family room and master bedroom, while a vaulted ceiling graces the living room. Built-ins, three fireplaces and a walk-in pantry add special touches. Every bedroom has walk-in closets, while the master bedroom's sitting area, upstairs library and versatile bonus room round out a home that is large on living and luxury.

(Left) The master bedroom's private porch is an intimate get-away.

(Right) A unique angled kitchen island provides a sink and a convenient eating area.

(Below Right) With a fireplace, built-ins and rich colors, this master bedroom is warm and inviting.

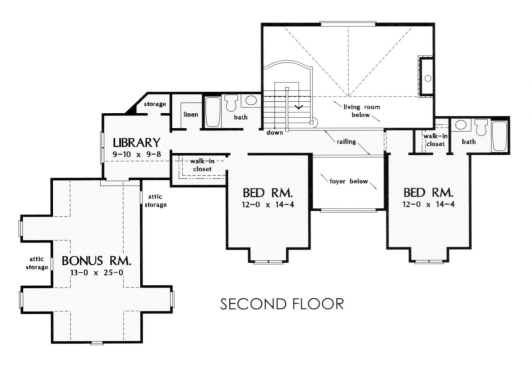

SECOND FLOOR

- LIBRARY 9-10 x 9-8
- storage
- linen
- bath
- down
- living room below
- railing
- walk-in closet
- bath
- walk-in closet
- foyer below
- attic storage
- attic storage
- BED RM. 12-0 x 14-4
- BED RM. 12-0 x 14-4
- BONUS RM. 13-0 x 25-0

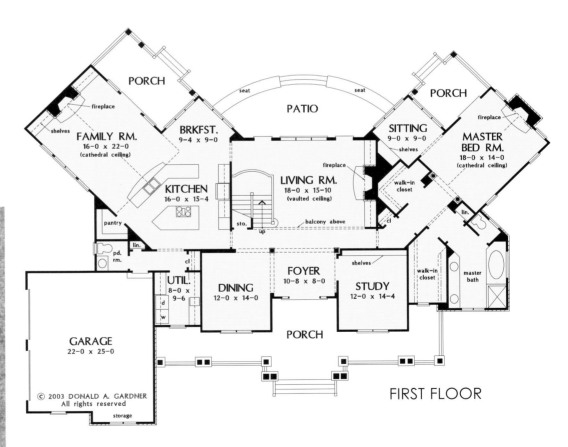

FIRST FLOOR

- PORCH
- fireplace
- shelves
- FAMILY RM. 16-0 x 22-0 (cathedral ceiling)
- KITCHEN 16-0 x 15-4
- pantry
- BRKFST. 9-4 x 9-0
- seat
- PATIO
- seat
- SITTING 9-0 x 9-0
- shelves
- PORCH
- fireplace
- MASTER BED RM. 18-0 x 14-0 (cathedral ceiling)
- LIVING RM. 18-0 x 15-10 (vaulted ceiling)
- fireplace
- walk-in closet
- cl
- balcony above
- up
- sto.
- pd. rm.
- lin.
- lin.
- master bath
- walk-in closet
- shelves
- cl
- UTIL. 8-0 x 9-6
- DINING 12-0 x 14-0
- FOYER 10-8 x 8-0
- STUDY 12-0 x 14-4
- GARAGE 22-0 x 25-0
- PORCH
- storage

© 2003 DONALD A. GARDNER
All rights reserved

Jerivale

Plan ATSDG01-1033

- Total Living: 3647 s.f.
- First Floor: 2766 s.f.
- Second Floor: 881 s.f.
- Bonus Room: 407 s.f.
- 3 Bedrooms, 3-1/2 Baths
- Width: 92'5"
- Depth: 71'10"
- Crawlspace Foundation
- Price Category F

1-800-388-7580
www.allthingssouthern.com

Photographed home may have been modified from
the original construction documents.

Rich with architectural detail, the great room is a perfect spot for entertaining.

RECALLING *Times Past*

My wife is from the city and I'm from the country, but we're both from the South. And we wanted a home that combined both rural and urban flair. We couldn't be happier with this plan. It marries a Traditional style with Country details such as dormers, metal roofs and stone.

This design takes a little of the Southeast and shares it with the rest of the regions. Twin dormers separate two sets of matching gables, and the study's exterior window is accented with a metal roof. Columns are used to define the dining room without enclosing space. While the master bath is crowned by a tray ceiling, the master bedroom and a secondary bedroom feature vaulted ceilings. A convenient pass-thru connects the kitchen to the great room, and the fireplace has built-in shelves on both sides. A sizable utility room is complete with counter space, and the garage includes a storage area. Above the garage, the bonus room awaits expansion needs.

Although the original plan calls for brick, the addition of stone to the façade is a welcome one.

www.allthingssouthern.com

BED RM.
12-8 x 12-0
(vaulted ceiling)

walk-in closet

BRKFST.
11-4 x 10-8

PORCH

MASTER BED RM.
14-0 x 16-0
(vaulted ceiling)

BED RM.
12-0 x 13-0

bath

KIT.
11-4 x 12-4

fireplace

GREAT RM.
16-8 x 19-4
(cathedral ceiling)

walk-in closet

walk-in closet

pantry

w   d

walk-in closet

UTIL.
11-0 x 6-0

shelves

seat

storage

up

pd. rm.

master bath

© 2001 DONALD A. GARDNER
All rights reserved

DINING
13-0 x 12-0

FOYER
6-0 x 12-0

cl

GARAGE
21-0 x 21-0

PORCH

STUDY
13-0 x 12-0

storage

FIRST FLOOR

Rear Rendering

© 2001 Donald A. Gardner, Inc.

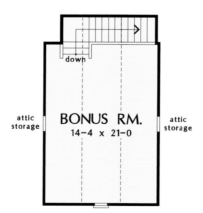

attic storage

BONUS RM.
14-4 x 21-0

attic storage

down

Yankton

Plan ATSDG01-933

- Total Living: 2330 s.f.
- Bonus Room: 346 s.f.
- 3 Bedrooms, 2 1/2 Baths
- Width: 62'3"
- Depth: 60'6"
- Crawlspace Foundation
- Price Category C

1-800-388-7580
www.allthingssouthern.com

(Above) Exposed wood and a box-bay window create a cozy ambiance. (Below) Rich red walls and French Provençal cabinetry define this efficient kitchen.

(Above) Open to the great room, the dining room is both practical and beautiful. (Below) A quiet sitting area adds another place to relax in the master bedroom.

cheerful DISPOSITION

A hip roof, brick veneer and arched windows lend an air of refinement to this stunning family home. The foyer, flanked by a dining room and bedroom/study, opens to a great room with sloped ceiling and clerestory window. Cathedral ceilings and arched windows bathe the dining room and breakfast room in natural light, while nine-foot ceilings add volume to the first level. The private master suite has a cathedral ceiling and sumptuous bath with whirlpool, shower and dual sink vanity. Two more bedrooms and a bonus room upstairs share a third bath.

Tall, dark green magnolia trees with big, bright white blooms envelope our home, accentuating the keystone arches, white trim and columns, while contrasting with the brick and siding. From the rocking chairs on the front porch, you can smell the sweet fragrances drift by on warm breezes.

(Opposite Page) This Traditional homes unites brick and siding with keystone arches and circletop transoms.

(This Page) Modified slightly from the original plan, the great room is the hub of family activity.

(Right) The dining room's cathedral ceiling adds impressive volume, enhancing visual space. Columns punctuate the entrance to this beautiful room.

(Below) The kitchen was modified to include a central island for a separate work station. Now, two or more cooks can function in the same space.

seat

spa

DECK

walk-in closet

MASTER BED RM.
15-8 x 13-4
(cathedral ceiling)

clerestory above

BRKFST.
12-0 x 10-8
(cathedral ceiling)

lin.

master bath

UTIL.
7-8 x 7-0

d   w   cl

fireplace

GREAT RM.
17-8 x 18-8

KITCHEN
12-0 x 13-0

bath

cl

up

cl

BED RM./ STUDY
11-0 x 12-6

FOYER
6-4 x 11-6

cl

DINING
12-0 x 13-4
(cathedral ceiling)

GARAGE
21-0 x 22-8

PORCH
19-0 x 7-0

storage

FIRST FLOOR

clerestory window with arched top

attic storage

skylight

bath

great room below

BED RM.
12-0 x 10-4

down

cl

down

cl

BED RM.
11-0 x 12-6
(cathedral ceiling)

attic storage

attic storage

attic storage

BONUS RM.
13-0 x 22-4

SECOND FLOOR

skylights

Irwin

Plan ATSDG01-297

- Total Living: 2130 s.f.
- First Floor: 1694 s.f.
- Second Floor: 436 s.f.
- Bonus Room: 345 s.f.
- 4 Bedrooms, 3 Baths
- Width: 54'0"
- Depth: 53'8"
- Crawlspace Foundation
- Price Category C

Photographed home may have been modified from the original construction documents.

there is a place
Donald A. Gardner Architects, Inc.

Jonesboro

*W*e wanted a home that reflects our Arkansas heritage…"the spirit of the river and the spirit of the lakes, the spirit in each and every home."

Plan ATSDG01-983

- Total Living: 1700 s.f.
- Bonus Room: 333 s.f.
- 3 Bedrooms, 2 Baths
- Width: 49'0"
- Depth: 65'4"
- Crawlspace Foundation
- Price Category B

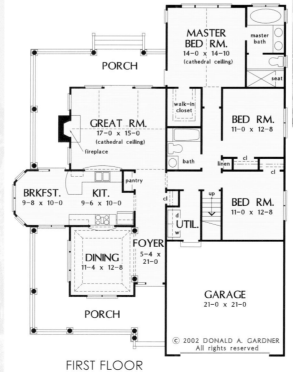

FIRST FLOOR

PORCH

MASTER BED RM.
14-0 x 14-10
(cathedral ceiling)

master bath

GREAT RM.
17-0 x 15-0
(cathedral ceiling)

fireplace

walk-in closet

BED RM.
11-0 x 12-8

bath

linen

BRKFST.
9-8 x 10-0

KIT.
9-6 x 10-0

pantry

up

BED RM.
11-0 x 12-8

UTIL.

DINING
11-4 x 12-8

FOYER
5-4 x 21-0

GARAGE
21-0 x 21-0

PORCH

REAR ELEVATION

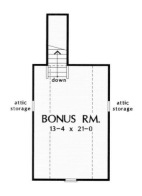

attic storage

BONUS RM.
13-4 x 21-0

down

attic storage

1-800-388-7580
www.allthingssouthern.com

*Q*uarried from North Carolina, the stone on our house creates an Old World impression used to influence both the Old and New South.

Luxembourg

Plan ATSDG01-979

- Total Living: 1797 s.f.
- First Floor: 1345 s.f.
- Second Floor: 452 s.f.
- Bonus Room: 349 s.f.
- 3 Bedrooms, 2 1/2 Baths
- Width: 63'0"
- Depth: 40'0"
- Crawlspace Foundation
- Price Category B

SECOND FLOOR

FIRST FLOOR

REAR ELEVATION

1-800-388-7580
www.allthingssouthern.com

Bookworth

From Faulkner and Williams to Twain, O'Connor and others, the South has created its own genre that can transcend boundaries, much like its architecture.

Plan ATSDG01-1027

- Total Living: 1820 s.f.
- 3 Bedrooms, 2 Baths
- Width: 61'10"
- Depth: 62'6"
- Crawlspace Foundation
- Price Category B

GARAGE
22-0 x 22-0

PORCH

UTIL.
12-2 x 6-0   w d

PORCH

MASTER BED RM.
12-0 x 14-0

fireplace

GREAT RM.
16-0 x 17-0
(cathedral ceiling)

BRKFST.
12-0 x 7-8

BED RM.
12-0 x 11-6

walk-in closet

walk-in closet

KITCHEN
12-0 x 11-8

lin.

bath

FOYER
9-4 x 5-8

cl

cl

master bath
(vaulted ceiling)

PORCH

DINING
12-0 x 13-0
(vaulted ceiling)

BED RM.
12-0 x 11-8

seat

FIRST FLOOR

REAR ELEVATION

Around our house, climbing roses and Confederate Jessamine soften the stone façade while lending greenery, subtle color and fragrances to the railing on the front porch.

Wilshire

Plan ATSDG01-976

- Total Living: 1904 s.f.
- Bonus Room: 366 s.f.
- 3 Bedrooms, 2 Baths
- Width: 53'10"
- Depth: 57'8"
- Crawlspace Foundation
- Price Category B

BONUS RM.
13-6 x 24-8

down

attic storage   attic storage

DINING
11-0 x 13-0

BRKFST.
9-8 x 8-0

PORCH

MASTER BED RM.
16-2 x 13-0

KITCHEN
15-8 x 11-0

fireplace

walk-in closet   walk-in closet

GREAT RM.
16-8 x 17-8
(12' ceiling)

bath

master bath

shelves

w   d

pan.

UTILITY
9-8 x 6-4

lin.

up

cl

FOYER
6-8 x 10-4

BED RM./ STUDY
12-0 x 12-0

cl

BED RM.
12-6 x 12-0

GARAGE
21-0 x 21-0

sto.

PORCH

FIRST FLOOR

REAR ELEVATION

there is a place

Donald A. Gardner Architects, Inc.

Kendleton

"*A mile or two" is "next door" in country terms, so here we are, next door to a country church. Sometimes choir practice drifts in through open windows.*

Plan ATSDG01-1058

- Total Living: 2036 s.f.
- Bonus Room: 506 s.f.
- 3 Bedrooms, 2 Baths
- Width: 52'0"
- Depth: 72'8"
- Crawlspace Foundation
- Price Category C

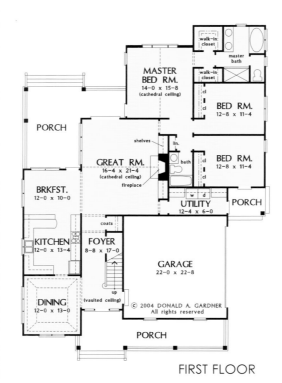

FIRST FLOOR

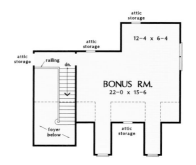

REAR ELEVATION

The design featured decorative wood brackets in the front gables, but in keeping with our Louisiana upbringing, we decided to add scrolled metalwork.

Fernley

Plan ATSDG01-980

- Total Living: 2037 s.f.
- Bonus Room: 361 s.f.
- 3 Bedrooms, 2 1/2 Baths
- Width: 62'4"
- Depth: 61'8"
- Crawlspace Foundation
- Price Category C

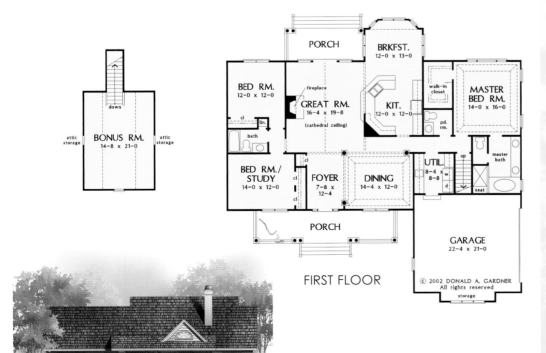

BONUS RM.
14-8 x 21-0

attic storage

down

BED RM.
12-0 x 12-0

fireplace

GREAT RM.
16-4 x 19-8
(cathedral ceiling)

cl

lin.

bath

BED RM./ STUDY
14-0 x 12-0

cl

cl

FOYER
7-8 x 12-4

DINING
14-4 x 12-0

PORCH

BRKFST.
12-0 x 13-0

KIT.
12-0 x 12-0

walk-in closet

pd. rm.

MASTER BED RM.
14-0 x 16-0

UTIL.
8-4 x 8-8

w
d

up

seat

master bath

PORCH

GARAGE
22-4 x 21-0

storage

FIRST FLOOR

REAR ELEVATION

Dayton

My great-grandfather was a state senator who brought about some wonderful changes. The times keep changing, but the architecture remains timeless.

Plan ATSDG01-1008

- Total Living: 2073 s.f.
- First Floor: 1569 s.f.
- Second Floor: 504 s.f.
- Bonus Room: 320 s.f.
- 3 Bedrooms, 2 1/2 Baths
- Width: 47'0"
- Depth: 55'0"
- Crawlspace Foundation
- Price Category C

MASTER BED RM.
14-8 x 14-0
(vaulted ceiling)

BRKFST.
12-0 x 11-8

PORCH

walk-in closet

cl

lin.

KIT.
12-0 x 10-8

fireplace

GREAT RM.
16-10 x 18-0
(vaulted ceiling)

master bath

UTIL.
5-10 x 5-8

pd. rm.

sto.

up

FOYER
7-6 x 9-8
(vaulted ceiling)

cl

DINING
11-8 x 13-8

GARAGE
22-0 x 22-0

PORCH

FIRST FLOOR

shelf

attic storage

walk-in closet

bath

great room below

BED RM.
11-0 x 12-0

down

down

lin.

cl

shelf

attic storage

BONUS RM.
13-4 x 22-0
(vaulted ceiling)

attic storage

BED RM.
11-8 x 11-4
(vaulted ceiling)

foyer below

SECOND FLOOR

REAR ELEVATION

It might sound trite, but country homes exude charm. Even if they're brand new, they have a character that makes them look like they've been around a while.

Northwyke

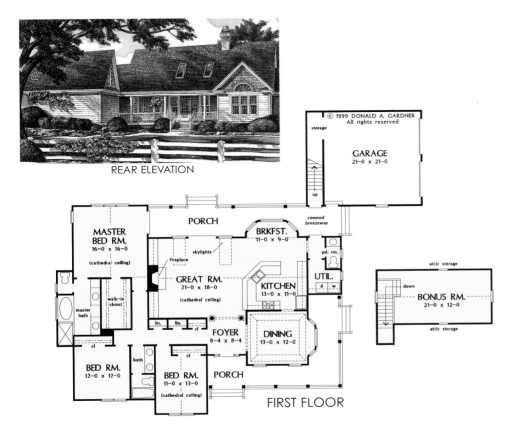

REAR ELEVATION

GARAGE
21-0 x 21-0

storage

up

covered breezeway

PORCH

BRKFST.
11-0 x 9-0

pd. rm.

MASTER
BED RM.
16-0 x 16-0
(cathedral ceiling)

skylights

fireplace

GREAT RM.
21-0 x 18-0
(cathedral ceiling)

KITCHEN
13-0 x 11-0

UTIL.
d   w

walk-in closet

master bath

lin.   lin.

cl

attic storage

down

BONUS RM.
21-0 x 12-0

attic storage

cl

FOYER
8-4 x 8-4

DINING
13-0 x 12-0

BED RM.
12-0 x 12-0

bath

cl

BED RM.
11-0 x 13-0
(cathedral ceiling)

PORCH

FIRST FLOOR

Plan ATSDG01-759

- Total Living: 2078 s.f.
- Bonus Room: 339 s.f.
- 3 Bedrooms, 2 1/2 Baths
- Width: 62'2"
- Depth: 47'8"
- Crawlspace Foundation
- Price Category C

1-800-388-7580
www.allthingssouthern.com

85

there is a place
Donald A. Gardner Architects, Inc.

Madaridge

A Country porch, Craftsman exterior and Traditional form create an expressive façade that exemplifies the way the South combines styles, and it works.

Plan ATSDG01-974

- Total Living: 2111 s.f.
- First Floor: 1496 s.f.
- Second Floor: 615 s.f.
- Bonus Room: 277 s.f.
- 3 Bedrooms, 2 1/2 Baths
- Width: 40'4"
- Depth: 70'0"
- Crawlspace Foundation
- Price Category C

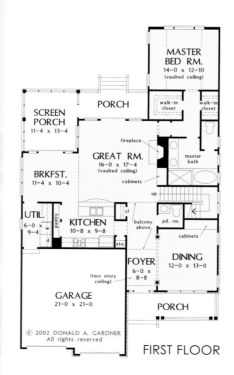

FIRST FLOOR

SECOND FLOOR

REAR ELEVATION

We placed statuary throughout our yard, and it really correlates with the stonework on our home, giving it an old Savannah look and feel.

Xavier

Plan ATSDG01-960

- Total Living: 2174 s.f.
- Bonus Room: 299 s.f.
- 4 Bedrooms, 3 Baths
- Width: 66'8"
- Depth: 56'6"
- Crawlspace Foundation
- Price Category C

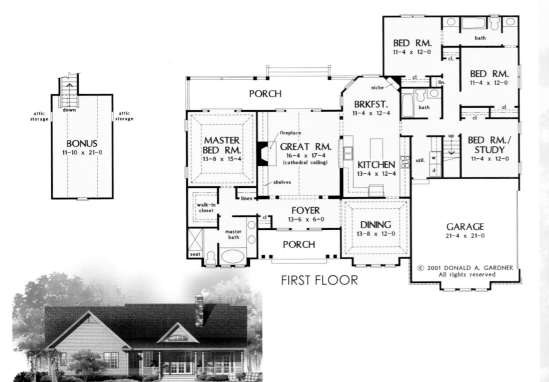

BONUS
11-10 x 21-0

attic storage   attic storage

down

FIRST FLOOR

PORCH

MASTER BED RM.
13-8 x 15-4

GREAT RM.
16-4 x 17-4
(cathedral ceiling)

fireplace

shelves

linen

walk-in closet

master bath

seat

FOYER
13-6 x 6-0

PORCH

DINING
13-8 x 12-0

BRKFST.
11-4 x 12-4

niche

KITCHEN
13-4 x 12-4

util.

up

w d

BED RM.
11-4 x 12-0

bath

BED RM.
11-4 x 12-0

BED RM./STUDY
11-4 x 12-0

lin.

bath

cl

GARAGE
21-4 x 21-0

REAR ELEVATION

© 2004 Donald A. Gardner, Inc.

Chalkrock

M etal roofs welcome the rain with a symphonic hammering that lulls you to sleep, or at least, to a more relaxing state of mind.

Plan ATSDG01-1054

- Total Living: 2231 s.f.
- First Floor: 1699 s.f.
- Second Floor: 532 s.f.
- Bonus Room: 549 s.f.
- 3 Bedrooms, 2 1/2 Baths
- Width: 48'10"
- Depth: 73'2"
- Crawlspace Foundation
- Price Category C

FIRST FLOOR

© 2004 DONALD A. GARDNER
All rights reserved

SECOND FLOOR

REAR ELEVATION

Envisioning laundry drying in the sun, we thought about farm life when we saw this house. It has old-time character for such a modern design.

Trotterville

Plan ATSDG01-984

- Total Living: 2490 s.f.
- First Floor: 1687 s.f.
- Second Floor: 803 s.f.
- 4 Bedrooms, 2 1/2 Baths
- Width: 52'8"
- Depth: 67'0"
- Crawlspace Foundation
- Price Category C

SECOND FLOOR

BED RM.
11-4 x 12-8

great room below

attic storage

BED RM.
12-0 x 11-0

railing

bath

lin.

BED RM.
12-8 x 11-0

foyer below

attic storage

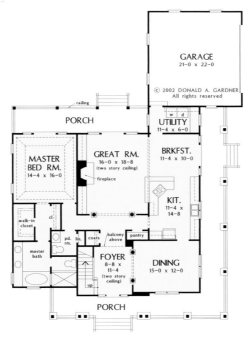

FIRST FLOOR

GARAGE
21-0 x 22-0

PORCH

UTILITY
11-4 x 6-0

MASTER BED RM.
14-4 x 16-0

GREAT RM.
16-0 x 18-8
(two story ceiling)
fireplace

BRKFST.
11-4 x 10-0

KIT.
11-4 x 14-8

walk-in closet

pd. rm.

lin.

coats

balcony above

pantry

master bath

FOYER
8-8 x 11-4
(two story ceiling)

DINING
15-0 x 12-0

up

PORCH

REAR ELEVATION

Newcastle

A covered bridge leads up to our "Old Kentucky Home" on the hillside. Every time I see the stone and cedar shake I feel blessed.

Plan ATSDG01-994

- Total Living: 2515 s.f.
- First Floor: 1834 s.f.
- Second Floor: 681 s.f.
- Bonus Room: 365 s.f.
- 3 Bedrooms, 3 1/2 Baths
- Width: 50'8"
- Depth: 66'8"
- Crawlspace Foundation
- Price Category D

FIRST FLOOR

PORCH

MASTER BED RM. 15-0 x 15-0

GREAT RM. 20-0 x 17-0 (vaulted ceiling)

fireplace

BRKFST. 12-0 x 11-0

KITCHEN 14-0 x 13-8

walk-in closet

walk-in closet

master bath

UTILITY 9-0 x 8-0

pd. rm.

sto.

up

FOYER 6-8 x 9-6

DINING 14-0 x 13-4

storage

GARAGE 21-0 x 21-0

SECOND FLOOR

attic storage

attic storage

desk

desk

BED RM. 15-0 x 11-0 (vaulted ceiling)

great room below

BED RM. 14-0 x 11-0 (vaulted ceiling)

bath

bath

down

railing

lin.

9-8 x 13-8

attic storage

foyer below

attic storage

down

BONUS RM. 11-8 x 16-4

attic storage

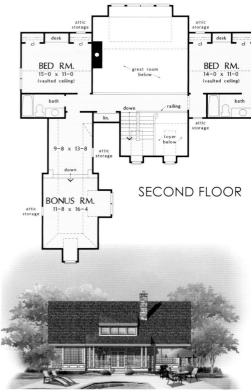

REAR ELEVATION

*M*ost places in the South have four distinct seasons, and with a wrapping front porch and rear screened porch, our home takes advantage of all of them.

Magnolia

Plan ATSDG01-544

- Total Living: 2617 s.f.
- First Floor: 1878 s.f.
- Second Floor: 739 s.f.
- Bonus Room: 383 s.f.
- 4 Bedrooms, 3 Baths
- Width: 79'8"
- Depth: 73'4"
- Crawlspace Foundation
- Price Category D

SECOND FLOOR

FIRST FLOOR

REAR ELEVATION

Just Outside the Door

To say the South is geographically diverse is almost an understatement. The South includes chilly mountain peaks, toasty warm sand, deserted deserts, meandering rivers, rolling farmland and secluded swampland, along with bustling urban areas throughout. It's a unique region, and with four mild seasons, many are attracted to a Southern setting. Very few Southerners ever want to leave, because they appreciate that warm Southern sun and cool Southern rain. To take advantage of their setting, Southerners extend their living space beyond the doors of their homes, to their porches, yards and surroundings — whether natural or concrete. The homes in this section take living outdoors, broadening horizons.

The stars at night are big and bright...Sometimes the kids and I will sit quietly on either the front or back porch steps and look for shooting stars. They get so excited every time they see one, and squeal with delight if more than one of us sees it, too.

COUNTRY
aspirations

This beautiful farmhouse with prominent twin gables and bays adds just the right amount of Country style to modern family life. The master suite is quietly tucked away downstairs with no bedrooms directly above, and the cook of the family will love the spacious U-shaped kitchen with ample cabinets and pantry. The bonus room is easily accessible from the back stairs or second floor, where three large bedrooms share two full baths. Storage space abounds with walk-ins, hall shelves and a linen closet upstairs. A curved balcony borders a versatile loft/study that overlooks a stunning two-story great room.

(Opposite page) This farmhouse greets family and friends with a large front porch and wide entryway.

(Above Left) The counter works as a serving bar for casual meals.

(Above Right) French doors lead out the dining room to the front porch for coffee and fresh air.

(Left) The living room acts as an old-fashioned parlor, connecting to the front porch through French doors.

A curved balcony overlooks the great room, visually connecting both floors.

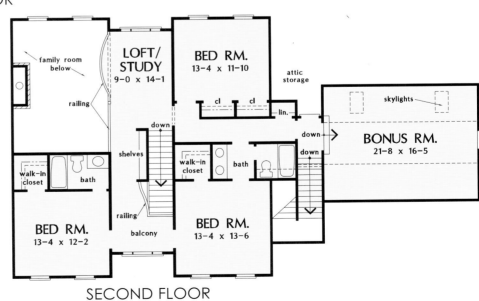

Rear Rendering

© 1996 Donald A. Gardner Architects, Inc.

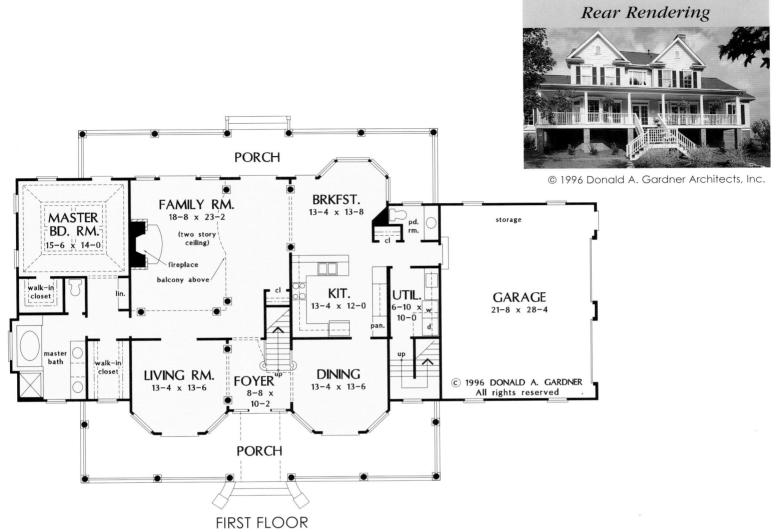

PORCH

MASTER BD. RM.
15-6 x 14-0

FAMILY RM.
18-8 x 23-2
(two story ceiling)

fireplace
balcony above

BRKFST.
13-4 x 13-8

pd. rm.

cl

storage

walk-in closet

lin.

cl

KIT.
13-4 x 12-0

UTIL.
6-10 x 10-0

w
d

pan.

GARAGE
21-8 x 28-4

master bath

walk-in closet

LIVING RM.
13-4 x 13-6

FOYER
8-8 x 10-2

up

DINING
13-4 x 13-6

up

PORCH

FIRST FLOOR

SECOND FLOOR

family room below

railing

LOFT/ STUDY
9-0 x 14-1

BED RM.
13-4 x 11-10

attic storage

cl   cl

lin.

skylights

down

BONUS RM.
21-8 x 16-5

shelves

down

walk-in closet

bath

walk-in closet

bath

down

BED RM.
13-4 x 12-2

railing

balcony

BED RM.
13-4 x 13-6

down

Arbordale

Plan ATSDG01-452

- Total Living: 3163 s.f.
- First Floor: 2086 s.f.
- Second Floor: 1077 s.f.
- Bonus Room: 403 s.f.
- 4 Bedrooms, 3 1/2 Baths
- Width: 81'10"
- Depth: 51'8"
- Crawlspace Foundation
- Price Category E

1-800-388-7580
www.allthingssouthern.com

Photographed home may have been modified from the original construction documents.

hillside Estate

(Opposite Page) A screened porch with fireplace creates an outdoor four-season room.

(This Page) A three-car garage and prominent gable with decorative bracket give this home a ranch appearance.

© 1998 Donald A. Gardner, Inc.

A stunning center dormer with arched window and decorative wood brackets cap the entry to this extraordinary hillside estate. Exposed wood beams enhance the magnificent cathedral ceilings of the foyer, great room, dining room, master bedroom and screened porch, while ten-foot ceilings top the remainder of the first floor. The great room takes in scenic rear views through a wall of windows shared by the media/rec room. Fireplaces add warmth and ambience to the great room, media/rec room, screened porch and the master suite's study/sitting area. The kitchen is complete with a center island cooktop, pantry and ample room for two or more cooks. A three-and-a-half-car garage allows space for storage or a golf cart.

(Left) The great room sitting area features a balcony, which overlooks the media/rec room.

(Below Left) The master bedroom opens to its own private study/sitting area.

(Below Right) Exposed beams and a striking stone fireplace bring the outdoors inside the home.

PORCH

media/rec. room below

PORCH

MASTER BED RM.
15-0 x 15-0
(cathedral ceiling)

railing

fireplace

SCREEN PORCH
14-10 x 15-6
(cathedral ceiling)

DINING
15-8 x 15-8
(cathedral ceiling)

GREAT RM.
21-8 x 21-0
(cathedral ceiling)

STUDY/ SITTING
12-4 x 16-0

linen

master bath

exposed beams

fireplace

fireplace

wet bar

oven

walk-in closet

built-in cab.

railing

down

sto.

PORCH

pd. rm.

KITCHEN
15-8 x 13-2

FOYER
21-8 x 5-6

walk-in closet

cl

cl

cl

BED RM.
12-0 x 14-0

cl

pan.

PORCH

LAUNDRY
10-6 x 12-2

d
w

BED RM.
12-0 x 14-0

bath

FIRST FLOOR

GARAGE
23-7 x 35-7

STORAGE/ GOLF CART
11-4 x 8-0

Rear Rendering

COVERED PATIO

balcony above

COVERED PATIO

BED RM.
13-0 x 15-8

MEDIA/ REC. RM.
21-8 x 24-0

fireplace

BED RM.
22-3 x 15-10

cl

bath

pd. rm.

wet bar

up

lin.

bath

walk-in closet

STORAGE
(unfinished)

MECHANICAL
23-5 x 22-2

BASEMENT FLOOR

Crowne Canyon

Plan ATSDG01-732

- Total Living: 4776 s.f.
- First Floor: 3040 s.f.
- Basement Floor: 1736 s.f.
- 5 Bedrooms, 4 Full and Two 1/2 Baths
- Width: 106'5"
- Depth: 104'2"
- Hillside Walkout Foundation
- Price Category H

1-800-388-7580
www.allthingssouthern.com

Photographed home may have been modified from the original construction documents.

Ready, set, grow with this lovely Country farmhouse wreathed in windows and a covered wraparound porch. A Palladian window in the clerestory dormer bathes the two-story foyer in natural light. Nine-foot ceilings throughout the first level, except kitchen, add drama.

The private, first-floor master suite has it all: whirlpool tub, shower, double lavs and large walk-in closet. Upstairs, two bedrooms with dormers and attic storage access share a full bath. Families can keep growing with the skylit bonus space over the garage.

Noble *Countryside*

Bobwhites, honeybees and swallowtails are just as important to our surroundings as deer, raccoons and our famous Tennessee Walking Horses. We fill our hanging baskets with flowers that attract the bees and butterflies and make sure the quail always have some brush in the field.

(Opposite Page) Rocking chairs and a container garden add charm to this country porch.

(Above) Stately columns and a trio of gables give architectural character to this façade.

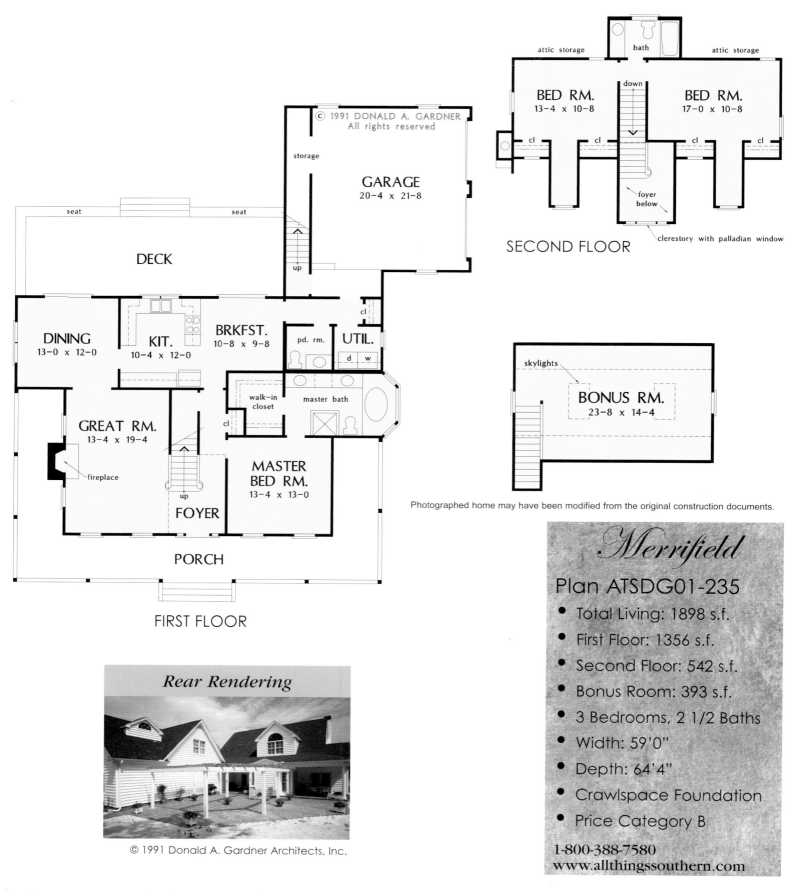

GARAGE
20-4 x 21-8

storage

seat   seat

DECK

up

DINING
13-0 x 12-0

KIT.
10-4 x 12-0

BRKFST.
10-8 x 9-8

pd. rm.

UTIL.

cl

d   w

walk-in closet

master bath

GREAT RM.
13-4 x 19-4

cl

fireplace

up

MASTER BED RM.
13-4 x 13-0

FOYER

PORCH

FIRST FLOOR

attic storage   bath   attic storage

BED RM.
13-4 x 10-8

down

BED RM.
17-0 x 10-8

cl   cl   cl   cl

foyer below

SECOND FLOOR

clerestory with palladian window

skylights

BONUS RM.
23-8 x 14-4

Photographed home may have been modified from the original construction documents.

Rear Rendering

Merrifield

Plan ATSDG01-235

- Total Living: 1898 s.f.
- First Floor: 1356 s.f.
- Second Floor: 542 s.f.
- Bonus Room: 393 s.f.
- 3 Bedrooms, 2 1/2 Baths
- Width: 59'0"
- Depth: 64'4"
- Crawlspace Foundation
- Price Category B

1-800-388-7580
www.allthingssouthern.com

(Above) The spacious great room offers plenty of room for entertaining guests or unwinding alone.

(Left) The kitchen and breakfast area combine to create an open, casual living space.

© 1999 Donald A. Gardner, Inc.

Revealing View

This Craftsman-style home takes advantage of hillside views with its deck, patio and abundance of rear windows. An open floor plan enhances the home's spaciousness. The great room features a cathedral ceiling, a fireplace with built-in cabinets and shelves, and access to the generous rear deck. Designed for ultimate efficiency, the kitchen serves the great room, dining room and breakfast area with equal ease. A tray ceiling lends elegance to the master bedroom, which features deck access, his-and-her walk-in closets and an extravagant bath with dual vanities, large linen closet, and separate tub and shower. A second master bedroom is located on the opposite side of the house and enjoys its own private bath, tray ceiling and deck access. Downstairs, a spacious family room with fireplace, a third bedroom and full bath complete the plan, creating a perfect area for guests.

We have a creek that winds around our property, and on Saturdays, the kids get up early, grab their poles from the storage area and walk down to the creek to fish. They never really catch anything with their poles, but their nets caught a few minnows for our koi pond one summer.

(Opposite Page) Gables, highlighted by decorative wood brackets, mimic the surrounding mountains.

(This Page) This porch accesses the guest bedroom through French doors.

(Above) A clerestory window opens the great room to the outdoors.

(Right) Inviting openness and conversation, a counter is all that separates the kitchen from the breakfast nook.

DECK

BRKFST.
13-4 x 10-2

BED RM.
15-0 x 14-8

cl

bath

lin.

pd. rm.

KITCHEN
13-4 x 11-4

pan.

w d

UTILITY
10-0 x 8-0

cl

© 1999 DONALD A. GARDNER
All rights reserved

GARAGE
21-0 x 23-2

storage

GREAT RM.
19-0 x 19-4

(cathedral ceiling)

fireplace

railing

down

MASTER BED RM.
15-0 x 17-0

walk-in closet

walk-in closet

lin.

master bath

FOYER
7-8 x 9-2

cl

DINING
13-4 x 12-0

PORCH

FIRST FLOOR

PATIO

UNFIN. STORAGE/ MECHANICAL
28-4 x 18-8

FAMILY RM.
19-0 x 18-6

fireplace

BED RM.
14-6 x 15-0

cl

lin.

bath

up

BASEMENT FLOOR

Heathridge

Plan ATSDG01-763

- Total Living: 2998 s.f.
- Basement Floor: 930 s.f.
- 3 Bedrooms, 3 1/2 Baths
- Width: 72'4"
- Depth: 66'0"
- Hillside Walkout Foundation
- Price Category D

1-800-388-7580
www.allthingssouthern.com

just outside the door
Donald A. Gardner Architects, Inc.

Sanibel

*W*e took concrete pillars, spheres and statues, and scattered them throughout our land-scaping. They make our house seem as if it's from another era.

Plan ATSDG01-541

- Total Living: 1954 s.f.
- 4 Bedrooms, 2 1/2 Baths
- Width: 65'2"
- Depth: 59'2"
- Crawlspace Foundation
- Price Category B

REAR ELEVATION

FIRST FLOOR

SCREEN PORCH
24–11 x 8–7
(12' ceiling)

BRKFST.
11–8 x 9–0
(12' ceiling)

MASTER BED RM.
15–0 x 13–4

fireplace

GREAT RM.
19–0 x 15–0
(12' ceiling)

KIT.
11–8 x 11–8
(12' ceiling)

bath

BED RM.
11–0 x 12–0

pan.

(8' high wall)

master bath

walk-in closet

FOYER
6–0 x 7–4

DINING
11–0 x 12–0
(12' ceiling)

pd. rm.

w d lin.

BED RM.
12–0 x 11–0

STUDY/ BED RM.
11–4 x 12–0
(10' ceiling)

PORCH

© 1997 DONALD A. GARDNER
All rights reserved

GARAGE
21–8 x 22–10

(optional full bath)

Draped with Spanish moss, a grove of large, old oak trees creates an enchanting, almost mystical, canopy that leads to our driveway.

Morninglory

Plan ATSDG01-236

- Total Living: 1778 s.f.
- First Floor: 1325 s.f.
- Second Floor: 453 s.f.
- 3 Bedrooms, 2 1/2 Baths
- Width: 48'4"
- Depth: 40'4"
- Crawlspace Foundation
- Price Category B

SECOND FLOOR

FIRST FLOOR

REAR ELEVATION

just outside the door

Donald A. Gardner Architects, Inc.

Georgetown

Walking through a field near our home, we came across an old horseshoe, so we took it back and hung it over our front door.

Plan ATSDG01-393

- Total Living: 1832 s.f.
- Bonus Room: 425 s.f.
- 3 Bedrooms, 2 Baths
- Width: 65'4"
- Depth: 62'0"
- Crawlspace Foundation
- Price Category B

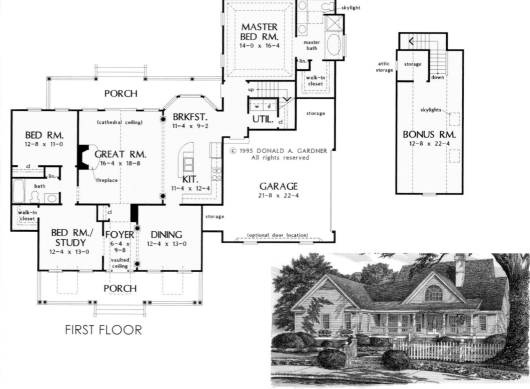

FIRST FLOOR

REAR ELEVATION

The South is more full of myths and legends than Alabama is of cottonseed. Every family has a unique story, and every home embraces them.

Drysdale

Plan ATSDG01-841

- Total Living: 1918 s.f.
- First Floor: 1412 s.f.
- Second Floor: 506 s.f.
- Bonus Room: 320 s.f.
- 3 Bedrooms, 2 1/2 Baths
- Width: 49'8"
- Depth: 52'0"
- Crawlspace Foundation
- Price Category B

FIRST FLOOR

SECOND FLOOR

just outside the door

Donald A. Gardner Architects, Inc.

Williamston

My grandparents had a home like this when I was young. We would sit on the porch and listen to the race every Sunday afternoon.

Plan ATSDG01-391

- Total Living: 1991 s.f.
- First Floor: 1480 s.f.
- Second Floor: 511 s.f.
- Bonus Room: 363 s.f.
- 3 Bedrooms, 2 1/2 Baths
- Width: 73'0''
- Depth: 45'0''
- Crawlspace Foundation
- Price Category B

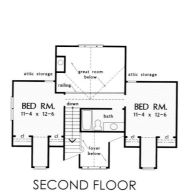

SECOND FLOOR

BED RM. 11-4 x 12-6
BED RM. 11-4 x 12-6
attic storage
great room below
railing
down
bath
foyer below

FIRST FLOOR

DECK
spa
GREAT RM. 15-4 x 19-2
BRKFST. 11-4 x 9-0
UTILITY 9-8 x 7-5
storage
GARAGE 20-4 x 25-8
MASTER BED RM. 14-4 x 16-2
fireplace (cathedral ceiling)
KIT. 11-4 x 12-2
balcony above
master bath
pd. rm.
FOYER 9-8 x 8-0
DINING 11-4 x 13-4
walk-in closet
up
PORCH

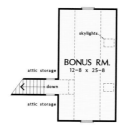

BONUS RM. 12-8 x 25-8
skylights
attic storage
down

REAR ELEVATION

We wanted to host an old-time square dance, so we cleared out the garage, brought in some straw bales and hired a bluegrass band.

Burgess

Plan ATSDG01-290

- Total Living: 2188 s.f.
- First Floor: 1618 s.f.
- Second Floor: 570 s.f.
- Bonus Room: 495 s.f.
- 3 Bedrooms, 2 1/2 Baths
- Width: 54'4"
- Depth: 57'0"
- Crawlspace Foundation
- Price Category C

BONUS RM.
15-4 x 25-8

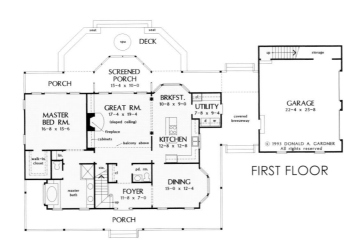

FIRST FLOOR

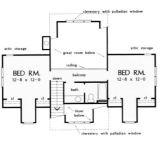

SECOND FLOOR

REAR ELEVATION

Palmetto

Reminding me of sweet, simpler days, Delta Blues cascade out my windows and onto the porch from an old phonograph that belonged to my grandmother.

Plan ATSDG01-737

- Total Living: 1843 s.f.
- First Floor: 1362 s.f.
- Second Floor: 481 s.f.
- 3 Bedrooms, 2 1/2 Baths
- Width: 49'4"
- Depth: 44'10"
- Post/Pier Foundation
- Price Category B

SECOND FLOOR

FIRST FLOOR

© 2003 Donald A. Gardner, Inc.

I couldn't get away for the entire weekend, so we put the tent in the backyard and had our own little camping trip right at home.

FIRST FLOOR

MASTER BED RM. 14-8 x 17-0
walk-in closet
walk-in closet
lin.
master bath
BRKFST. 10-0 x 9-0
PORCH
skylights
wet bar
shelves
(cathedral ceiling)
cl
BED RM. 11-0 x 13-0
KIT. 11-4 x 13-4
GREAT RM. 19-0 x 17-0
fireplace
BED RM. 13-0 x 11-0
cl
bath
UTIL. 7-4 x 7-0
d w
up
DINING 13-0 x 11-0
FOYER 6-4 x 11-0
BED RM./ STUDY 11-0 x 13-0
cl
cl
PORCH
GARAGE 22-0 x 22-0
storage

down
BONUS RM. 14-10 x 22-0 (cathedral ceiling)
attic storage
attic storage

Lilycrest

Plan ATSDG01-1022

- Total Living: 2243 s.f.
- Bonus Room: 332 s.f.
- 4 Bedrooms, 2 Baths
- Width: 62'0"
- Depth: 67'2"
- Crawlspace Foundation
- Price Category C

REAR ELEVATION

just outside the door

Donald A. Gardner Architects, Inc.

Hutchings

I couldn't throw away the broken plates. They held too much sentimental value, so we turned them into a mosaic tabletop and enjoy them everyday on the screened porch.

Plan ATSDG01-1057

- Total Living: 2278 s.f.
- Bonus Room: 306 s.f.
- 3 Bedrooms, 2 Baths
- Width: 61'7"
- Depth: 80'1"
- Crawlspace Foundation
- Price Category C

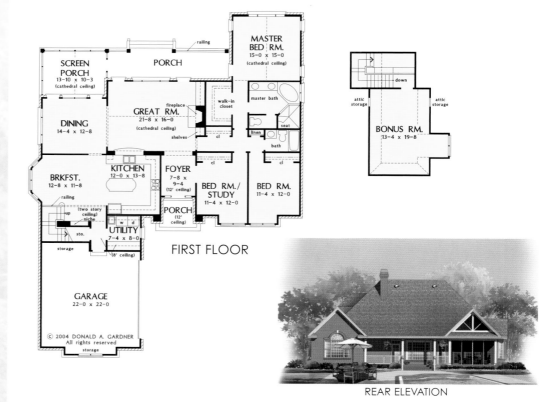

FIRST FLOOR

REAR ELEVATION

*W*ith a wrapping porch, we were able to place our herb garden containers where they would be accessible, yet receive the proper amount of sun and shade.

Peachtree

Plan ATSDG01-524

- Total Living: 2298 s.f.
- First Floor: 1743 s.f.
- Second Floor: 555 s.f.
- Bonus Room: 350 s.f.
- 4 Bedrooms, 3 Baths
- Width: 78'0"
- Depth: 53'2"
- Crawlspace Foundation
- Price Category C

BONUS RM.
12-0 x 20-8

down

SCREEN PORCH
20-8 x 9-6
(cathedral ceiling)

DECK

GARAGE
21-0 x 20-8

PORCH

walk-in closet

MASTER BED RM.
12-8 x 17-2

fireplace

GREAT RM.
15-4 x 19-4
(cathedral ceiling)

balcony above

BRKFST.
10-8 x 9-8

UTIL.
7-6 x 7-10

w   d

up

storage

KIT.
13-0 x 13-6

FIRST FLOOR

lin.

bath

master bath

BED RM./STUDY
12-8 x 11-4

cl

cl

up

lin.

FOYER
13-0 x 8-10
(vaulted ceiling)

DINING
12-8 x 12-8

PORCH

REAR ELEVATION

attic storage

great room below

attic storage

railing

BED RM.
12-8 x 12-0

balcony

down

BED RM.
12-8 x 12-0

bath

cl

cl

cl

cl

attic storage

foyer below

attic storage

SECOND FLOOR

Buena Vista

We often open the French doors to the back porch. The salty air and warm breezes freely move about our home, merging indoor and outdoor living.

Plan ATSDG01-911

- Total Living: 2599 s.f.
- First Floor: 1680 s.f.
- Second Floor: 919 s.f.
- 3 Bedrooms, 3 1/2 Baths
- Width: 51'8"
- Depth: 53'6"
- Post/Pier Foundation
- Price Category D

FIRST FLOOR

SECOND FLOOR

REAR ELEVATION

My favorite spot in the house would have to be our master bedroom's private balcony. We can soak up the sun or enjoy tranquil midnight breezes.

Seabrook

Plan ATSDG01-546

- Total Living: 2055 s.f.
- First Floor: 1366 s.f.
- Second Floor: 689 s.f.
- 3 Bedrooms, 2 Baths
- Width: 49'8"
- Depth: 50'6"
- Post/Pier Foundation
- Price Category C

BALCONY
12-4 x 6-4

MASTER
BED RM.
12-4 x 16-4

skylights

fireplace

(cathedral ceiling)

attic storage

walk-in closet

master bath

down   handrail

LOFT/
STUDY
10-1 x 11-4
(cathedral ceiling)

shelves

palladian window

SECOND FLOOR

PORCH

fireplace

GREAT RM.
14-0 x 16-0

© 1998 DONALD A. GARDNER
All rights reserved

BED RM.
12-0 x 11-0

KIT.
12-0 x 11-0

DINING
12-8 x 11-0

bath

pan.

walk-in closet   lin.

UTIL
6-0 x
8-0

FOYER
9-2 x 6-8

BED RM.
12-0 x 11-0
(cathedral ceiling)

w   d

down   up

down

PORCH

FIRST FLOOR

REAR ELEVATION

Edisto

From azaleas and gardenias to roses and hydrangeas, our garden incorporates an old-fashioned ambiance. Extending the garden to the porch, colorful annuals fill hanging baskets.

Plan ATSDG01-764

- Total Living: 2509 s.f.
- First Floor: 1830 s.f.
- Second Floor: 679 s.f.
- Bonus Room: 346 s.f.
- 4 Bedrooms, 4 Baths
- Width: 81'2"
- Depth: 48'0"
- Crawlspace Foundation
- Price Category D

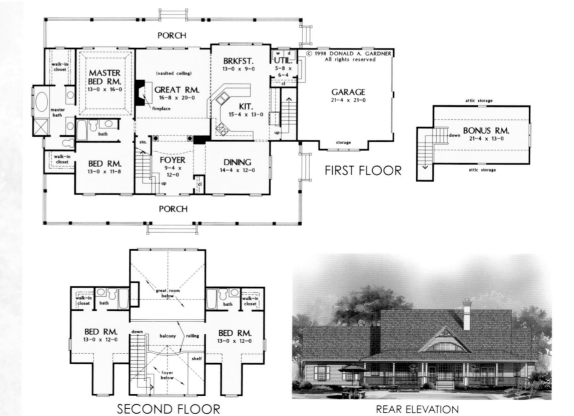

FIRST FLOOR

SECOND FLOOR

REAR ELEVATION

*W*ith soft outdoor pillows and a light throw, our porch swing is a great place to take a nap. My dog lies underneath it for her naps too.

Southerland

Plan ATSDG01-971

- Total Living: 2521 s.f.
- First Floor: 1798 s.f.
- Second Floor: 723 s.f.
- Bonus Room: 349 s.f.
- 4 Bedrooms, 3 1/2 Baths
- Width: 66'8"
- Depth: 49'8"
- Crawlspace Foundation
- Price Category D

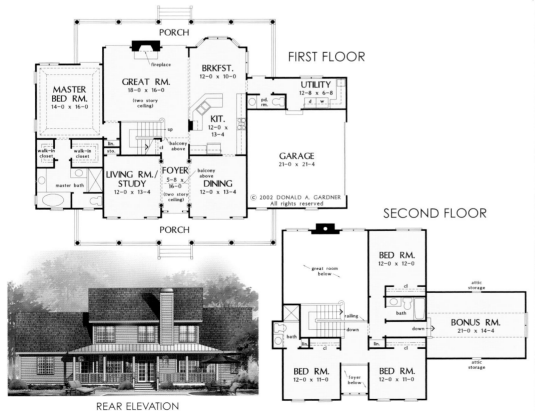

FIRST FLOOR

PORCH

fireplace

GREAT RM.
18-0 x 16-0
(two story ceiling)

BRKFST.
12-0 x 10-0

UTILITY
12-8 x 6-8

MASTER BED RM.
14-0 x 16-0

KIT.
12-0 x 13-4

pd. rm.

d w

walk-in closet

walk-in closet

lin.
sto.

up

balcony above

master bath

LIVING RM./STUDY
12-0 x 13-4

FOYER
5-8 x 16-0
(two story ceiling)

balcony above

DINING
12-0 x 13-4

GARAGE
21-0 x 21-4

PORCH

SECOND FLOOR

great room below

BED RM.
12-0 x 12-0

attic storage

railing

down

cl

bath

down

BONUS RM.
21-0 x 14-4

bath

lin.

cl

attic storage

BED RM.
12-0 x 11-0

foyer below

BED RM.
12-0 x 11-0

REAR ELEVATION

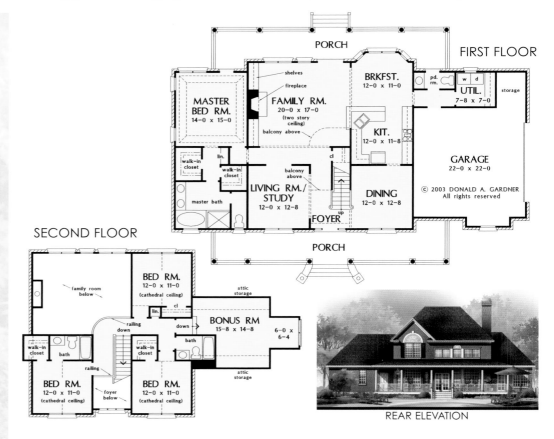

just outside the door
Donald A. Gardner Architects, Inc.

Peppermill

F̶or her birthday, each one of her grandchildren made her a stepping stone. The stepping stones lead from the back porch to her treasured "secret" garden.

Plan ATSDG01-1034

- Total Living: 2586 s.f.
- First Floor: 1809 s.f.
- Second Floor: 777 s.f.
- Bonus Room: 264 s.f.
- 4 Bedrooms, 3 1/2 Baths
- Width: 70'7"
- Depth: 48'4"
- Crawlspace Foundation
- Price Category D

FIRST FLOOR

PORCH

MASTER BED RM.
14-0 x 15-0

FAMILY RM.
20-0 x 17-0
(two story ceiling)
balcony above

shelves
fireplace

BRKFST.
12-0 x 11-0

pd. rm.

UTIL.
7-8 x 7-0
w d
storage

KIT.
12-0 x 11-8

walk-in closet
lin.
walk-in closet

balcony above

cl

GARAGE
22-0 x 22-0

LIVING RM./STUDY
12-0 x 12-8

master bath

DINING
12-0 x 12-8

FOYER
up

© 2003 DONALD A. GARDNER
All rights reserved

PORCH

SECOND FLOOR

family room below

BED RM.
12-0 x 11-0
(cathedral ceiling)

attic storage

lin.
cl

railing down

BONUS RM
15-8 x 14-8

down

6-0 x 6-4

bath

walk-in closet
bath

walk-in closet

railing

attic storage

BED RM.
12-0 x 11-0
(cathedral ceiling)

foyer below

BED RM.
12-0 x 11-0
(cathedral ceiling)

REAR ELEVATION

During football season, our American flag and state flag are accompanied by our college flag. All three have dedicated poles and are revered by our family and friends.

Hatteras

Plan ATSDG01-739

- Total Living: 2362 s.f.
- First Floor: 1650 s.f.
- Second Floor: 712 s.f.
- 3 Bedrooms, 2 1/2 Baths
- Width: 58'10"
- Depth: 47'4"
- Post/Pier Foundation
- Price Category C

SECOND FLOOR

BALCONY

BED RM.
13-4 x 12-4

BED RM.
11-0 x 13-4

cl

lin.

cl

bath

LOFT
11-2 x 13-8

railing

great room below

arched opening

down

FIRST FLOOR

BALCONY

DINING
11-0 x 13-4

down

PORCH

MASTER BED RM.
13-4 x 16-0

KIT.
11-0 x 12-8

fireplace

GREAT RM.
20-0 x 19-8
(cathedral ceiling)

STUDY
12-0 x 12-0

walk-in closet

walk-in closet

cl

down

FOYER
6-6 x 4-0

up

pd. rm.

cl

cl

UTIL.
6-0 x 6-0

linen

PORCH

d

w

master bath

down

REAR ELEVATION

just outside the door
Donald A. Gardner Architects, Inc.

Ventana

When we built the house, we had two metal pieces commissioned for our front porch, and we hung an old salvaged wrought-iron gate on a back porch wall.

Plan ATSDG01-336

- Total Living: 1929 s.f.
- 3 Bedrooms, 2 Baths
- Width: 59'0"
- Depth: 68'8"
- Crawlspace Foundation
- Price Category B

FIRST FLOOR

- covered porch
- DINING RM. 12-8 x 11-8
- skylights
- GREAT RM. 15-4 x 19-0
- master bath
- covered porch
- MASTER BED RM. 16-0 x 13-8
- lin.
- pantry
- desk
- fireplace
- (cathedral ceiling)
- walk-in closet
- lin.
- bath
- KITCHEN 19-0 x 12-4
- cl
- cl
- FOYER 9-8 x 5-8
- BED RM./ STUDY 11-4 x 11-8
- UTIL. 6-0 x 11-0 w d
- cl
- BED RM. 11-0 x 11-0
- BRKFST. 10-4 x 12-2
- storage
- GARAGE 19-8 x 23-0

REAR ELEVATION

1-800-388-7580
www.allthingssouthern.com

*W*e've decorated our porches with old rocking chairs and wicker. The distressed furniture features worn wood and chipped paint, creating a nostalgic feel.

Forrester

Plan ATSDG01-306

- Total Living: 3037 s.f.
- First Floor: 2316 s.f.
- Second Floor: 721 s.f.
- Bonus Room: 545 s.f.
- 4 Bedrooms, 3 1/2 Baths
- Width: 95'4"
- Depth: 54'10"
- Crawlspace Foundation
- Price Category E

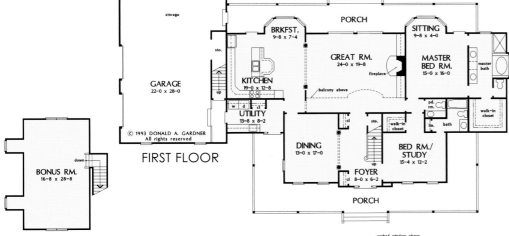

FIRST FLOOR

BONUS RM.
16-8 x 28-8

SECOND FLOOR

REAR ELEVATION

Lay My Burdens Down

Work hard; play hard. Early to rise and late to bed. Always make time for family and friends. If Southerners didn't invent these philosophies, they certainly perfected them. However when the day is over, and it's time to sleep, Southerners take their rest just as seriously as work or play. Bedrooms then become havens of rest and sanctuaries of comfort. Whether they include beautiful windows and ceiling treatments or incorporate private baths, the homes in this section showcase bedrooms that allow you to create your own private niche in the world — just like the South has created its own home in the hearts of so many.

Brick and siding combine curb appeal with low maintenance in this stately Traditional home. A Palladian window and bold columns add classic architectural interest. A sidelight and transom highlight the front door and allow natural light into the home. With tray ceilings in the dining room and master bedroom, along with a vaulted ceiling in the study/bedroom, this home showcases custom-styled elements. The family-efficient floor plan defines rooms without enclosing space. Note the savings on plumbing by having the kitchen, utility room and master bath adjacent to each other. For future expansion purposes, the bonus room staircase is located off the kitchen and garage, making the space perfect for a rec room, home office or gym.

© 2003 Donald A. Gardner, Inc.

The South has mountains, coasts, flatlands, desert, unspoiled country and metropolitan areas. We're lucky — or blessed. Sometimes I lie in bed and think about being able to experience so many different things without leaving this region. I guess that's an underlying element that makes Southerners proud of being Southern.

(Opposite Page) A three-tiered tray ceiling creates a dreamy ambiance in this master bedroom.

(Above) Tile and woodwork continue the tranquil theme in the master bath.

(Above Right) Brick and siding allow this Traditional home to fit in many streetscapes or lots.

The dining room welcomes guests as they enter the front door.

The cozy breakfast nook is brightened by windows.

The space-saving kitchen makes meal preparation easy and efficient.

Warm and inviting, the great room is a perfect place to unwind.

Rear Rendering

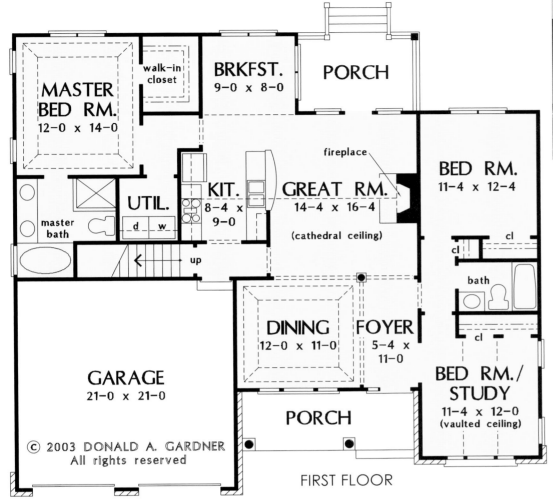

MASTER BED RM.
12-0 x 14-0

walk-in closet

BRKFST.
9-0 x 8-0

PORCH

master bath

UTIL.

d   w

KIT.
8-4 x 9-0

up

fireplace

GREAT RM.
14-4 x 16-4

(cathedral ceiling)

BED RM.
11-4 x 12-4

cl   cl

cl

bath

DINING
12-0 x 11-0

FOYER
5-4 x 11-0

cl

BED RM./ STUDY
11-4 x 12-0
(vaulted ceiling)

GARAGE
21-0 x 21-0

PORCH

FIRST FLOOR

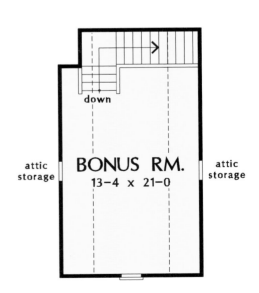

down

attic storage

BONUS RM.
13-4 x 21-0

attic storage

Photographed home may have been modified from the original construction documents.

Nicholson

Plan ATSDG01-1021

- Total Living: 1486 s.f.
- Bonus Room: 341 s.f.
- 3 Bedrooms, 2 Baths
- Width: 52'3"
- Depth: 46'10"
- Crawlspace Foundation
- Price Category A

1-800-388-7580
www.allthingssouthern.com

Sweet Dreams

Southern manors often revisit their Old World heritage with grand details and styling. Nearly a thing of the past, hardwood floors and fireplaces were once staples in almost every estate home that dotted the landscape, and we wanted to recreate the aura in our private master suite.

With Georgian-inspired details, this stately home has striking curb appeal.

Furniture-quality cabinetry and a cookbook library enhance the kitchen.

This home's commanding brick exterior with arch-topped windows, keystone arches, quoins, covered entry and hip roof creates a stunning presence, while its spacious interior is equally impressive. An exciting second-floor balcony overlooks the vaulted foyer and great room. Two sets of French doors flank the great room's fireplace and lead to the back porch and patio. Note the built-in shelves and clerestory dormer windows in the great room. The adjacent kitchen is generously proportioned, featuring a sizable work island and nearby built-in desk and walk-in pantry. A short hall provides extra privacy for the first-floor master suite, which enjoys a tray ceiling, fireplace, back-porch access, his-and-her walk-in closets and bath with garden tub. Upstairs, two secondary bedrooms have walk-in closets. The three-car garage includes additional space for storage.

(Left) A grand staircase makes a stunning impression in the foyer.

(Top Right) The study features heavy molding and a circletop transom.

(Bottom Right) French doors and transoms flank the great room's focal point — the fireplace.

Rear Rendering

© 2000 Donald A. Gardner, Inc.

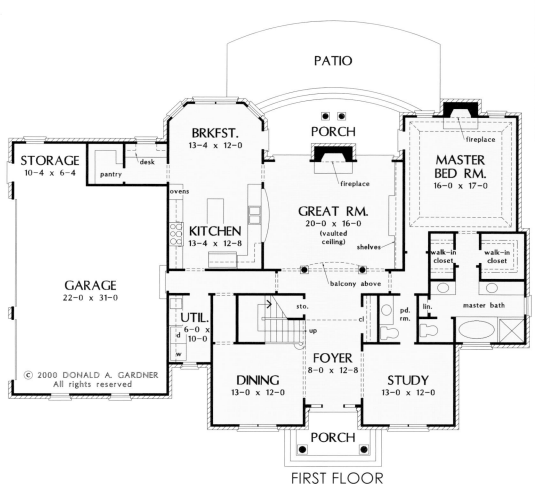

STORAGE
10-4 x 6-4

pantry

desk

BRKFST.
13-4 x 12-0

PORCH

fireplace

MASTER
BED RM.
16-0 x 17-0

fireplace

ovens

KITCHEN
13-4 x 12-8

GREAT RM.
20-0 x 16-0
(vaulted ceiling)

shelves

walk-in closet

walk-in closet

GARAGE
22-0 x 31-0

balcony above

master bath

© 2000 DONALD A. GARDNER
All rights reserved

UTIL.
6-0 x 10-0

sto.

up

cl

pd. rm.

lin.

DINING
13-0 x 12-0

FOYER
8-0 x 12-8

STUDY
13-0 x 12-0

PORCH

FIRST FLOOR

PATIO

Santerini

Plan ATSDG01-868

- Total Living: 2955 s.f.
- First Floor: 2270 s.f.
- Second Floor: 685 s.f.
- Bonus Room: 563 s.f.
- 3 Bedrooms, 2 1/2 Baths
- Width: 75'1"
- Depth: 53'6"
- Crawlspace Foundation
- Price Category D

1-800-388-7580
www.allthingssouthern.com

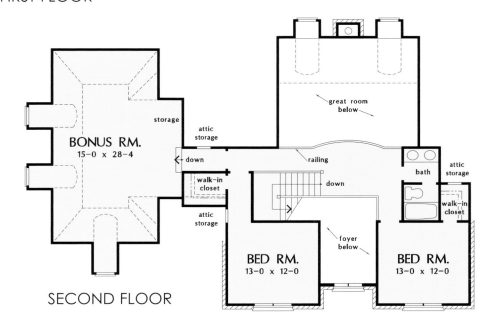

BONUS RM.
15-0 x 28-4

storage

attic storage

great room below

down

railing

bath

attic storage

walk-in closet

down

walk-in closet

attic storage

BED RM.
13-0 x 12-0

foyer below

BED RM.
13-0 x 12-0

SECOND FLOOR

Photographed home may have been modified from the original construction documents.

Two clerestory windows and cathedral ceilings increase the volume in the great room and sunroom.

The master suite features plentiful windows, a sitting area and fireplace.

Arched windows, interior and exterior columns, and brick veneer give this four-bedroom Traditional home instant authority. An arched clerestory window channels light from the foyer to the great room. Graceful columns punctuate the open interior that connects the foyer, great room, kitchen and sunroom. Special ceiling treatments and skylights add volume throughout the home. The master suite with fireplace, garden tub, separate shower and vanities, accesses the deck with optional spa. The skylit bonus room makes a great play area for kids and provides easy access to attic storage. Note the generous utility room with cabinetry.

touching clouds

When my wife and I got married, our first apartment was a small but charming studio in Atlanta. It had a fireplace in our living room / bedroom, and we got used to sleeping by the fire. So when we looked for a home to build, we both really wanted a fireplace in the master bedroom.

Twin gables and a hip roof create immediate symmetry.

(Left) A clerestory window, transoms and French doors flood the sunroom with natural light.

(Top Right) The bedroom/study provides a cozy place for reading and reflection.

(Bottom Right) Columns make a grand entrance into the kitchen, keeping it open to the great room.

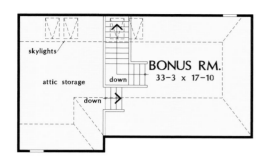

skylights

attic storage

BONUS RM.
33-3 x 17-10

down

down

seat

spa

DECK

fireplace

skylights

master bath

MASTER BED RM.
14-0 x 19-4

lin.

walk-in closet

arched window above door

SUN RM.
15-8 x 10-0
(cathedral ceiling)

skylights

BRKFST.
12-0 x 11-0

VESTIBULE

UTIL.
9-2 x 6-8

d w

storage

BED RM.
13-0 x 12-0

cl

GREAT RM.
18-0 x 21-0
(cathedral ceiling)

up

bath

fireplace

BED RM.
11-8 x 11-0

cabinets

KITCHEN
12-0 x 16-0

storage

GARAGE
21-0 x 23-0

walk-in closet

pd. rm.

sto.

cl

FOYER
12-0 x 5-8

© 1993 DONALD A. GARDNER
All rights reserved

cl

DINING
12-0 x 14-0

FIRST FLOOR

BED RM./ STUDY
12-0 x 12-0

PORCH
15-0 x 5-2

Herndon

Plan ATSDG01-302

- Total Living: 2663 s.f.
- Bonus Room: 653 s.f.
- 4 Bedrooms, 2 1/2 Baths
- Width: 72'7"
- Depth: 71'5"
- Crawlspace Foundation
- Price Category D

1-800-388-7580
www.allthingssouthern.com

Whimsical Rest

The tray ceiling visually lifts the master bedroom, accentuating the four-poster bed.

This updated farmhouse has plenty of square footage and custom-styled features. Twin gables, sidelights and an arched entryway accent the façade, while decorative ceiling treatments, bay windows and French doors adorn the interior. From an abundance of counter space and large walk-in pantry to the built-ins and storage areas, this design makes the most of space. Supported by columns, a curved balcony overlooks the stunning two-story great room. The powder room is easily accessible from the common rooms, and angled corners soften the dining room. An upstairs bedroom is equipped with its own bath, while two additional bedrooms share a full bath with the bonus room.

We wanted a ceiling that felt like the open country sky, and the tray ceiling gives us that feeling, yet adds a touch of elegance that I always wanted in a Southern manor. It seems that our poster bed reaches up toward the sky — almost like you're sleeping in a cloud.

The two-story great room showcases built-in cabinetry, a magnificent fireplace and curved balcony.

(Above) The formal living room/study keeps a natural traffic flow by connecting to the great room and foyer.

(Right) This brick farmhouse features curved transoms that echo the barrel-vault entry.

© 2001 Donald A. Gardner, Inc.

Rear Rendering

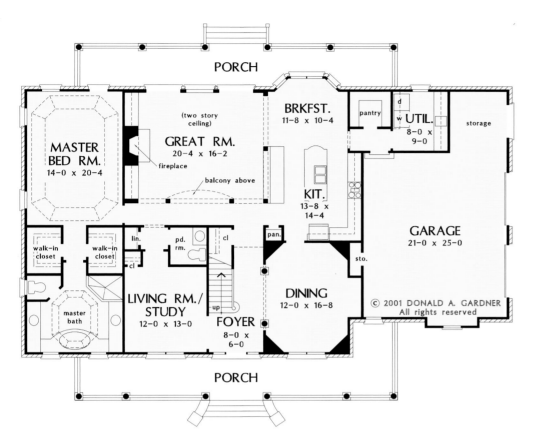

PORCH

GREAT RM.
20-4 x 16-2

(two story ceiling)

fireplace

balcony above

MASTER BED RM.
14-0 x 20-4

BRKFST.
11-8 x 10-4

pantry

d w **UTIL.**
8-0 x 9-0

storage

KIT.
13-8 x 14-4

GARAGE
21-0 x 25-0

walk-in closet

walk-in closet

lin.

cl

pd. rm.

cl

pan.

master bath

LIVING RM./ STUDY
12-0 x 13-0

up

FOYER
8-0 x 6-0

DINING
12-0 x 16-8

sto.

PORCH

FIRST FLOOR

Hickory Ridge

Plan ATSDG01-916

- Total Living: 3167 s.f.
- First Floor: 2194 s.f.
- Second Floor: 973 s.f.
- Bonus Room: 281 s.f.
- 4 Bedrooms, 3 1/2 Baths
- Width: 71'11"
- Depth: 54'4"
- Crawlspace Foundation
- Price Category E

1-800-388-7580
www.allthingssouthern.com

great room below

BED RM.
12-0 x 14-0

attic storage

cl

cl

railing

BONUS RM.
14-10 x 17-0

7-0 x 6-0

down

down

walk-in closet

bath

bath

walk-in closet

BED RM.
12-0 x 13-0

foyer below

BED RM.
12-0 x 13-0

attic storage

SECOND FLOOR

Photographed home may have been modified from the original construction documents.

Vandenberg

I love coming home on school breaks and vacations. My parents haven't really redecorated my room, but they enclosed my figurine collection in a glass case.

Plan ATSDG01-746

- Total Living: 2956 s.f.
- First Floor: 1810 s.f.
- Basement Floor: 1146 s.f.
- 4 Bedrooms, 3 Baths
- Width: 68'4"
- Depth: 60'10"
- Hillside Walkout Foundation
- Price Category D

REAR ELEVATION

FIRST FLOOR

BASEMENT FLOOR

© 2003 Donald A. Gardner, Inc.

We vacationed in one of Kentucky's historic Bed-n-Breakfasts that featured a bedroom with a cathedral ceiling and exposed beams, so we modified our bedroom to feature beams.

Hilligan

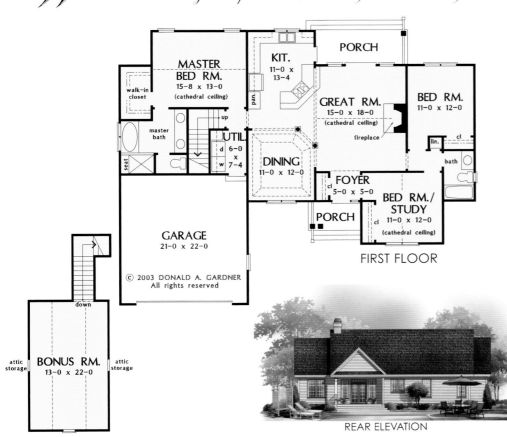

FIRST FLOOR

REAR ELEVATION

Plan ATSDG01-1015

- Total Living: 1535 s.f.
- Bonus Room: 355
- 3 Bedrooms, 2 Baths
- Width: 59'8"
- Depth: 47'4"
- Crawlspace Foundation
- Price Category B

Lay my burdens down
Donald A. Gardner Architects, Inc.

Iverson

They filmed a movie scene about the Revolutionary war in an empty field near my house. At night I could lie in bed and see the movie lights.

Plan ATSDG01-1023

- Total Living: 1547 s.f.
- Bonus Room: 391 s.f.
- 3 Bedrooms, 2 Baths
- Width: 51'8"
- Depth: 59'0"
- Crawlspace Foundation
- Price Category B

FIRST FLOOR

REAR ELEVATION

B efore they demolished our old barn, I salvaged a small piece of an old wall ~ sun-bleached, peeling paint and all. It proudly hangs in our bedroom.

Jarrell

Plan ATSDG01-1017

- Total Living: 1727 s.f.
- Bonus Room: 346 s.f.
- 3 Bedrooms, 2 Baths
- Width: 46'0"
- Depth: 66'4"
- Crawlspace Foundation
- Price Category B

BONUS RM.
13-4 x 22-0

attic storage

attic storage

down

FIRST FLOOR

SCREEN PORCH
17-8 x 10-0

DINING
11-0 x 12-4

MASTER BED RM.
16-4 x 14-8

walk-in closet

linen

cl

GREAT RM.
17-2 x 19-4
(cathedral ceiling)

fireplace

KIT.
11-0 x 12-4
(cathedral ceiling)

master bath

seat

bath

cabinets

FOYER
7-4 x 6-8

coats

cl

BEDROOM/STUDY
11-0 x 12-4

UTIL.
w
d

up

BED RM.
11-0 x 12-4

PORCH

GARAGE
21-0 x 22-0

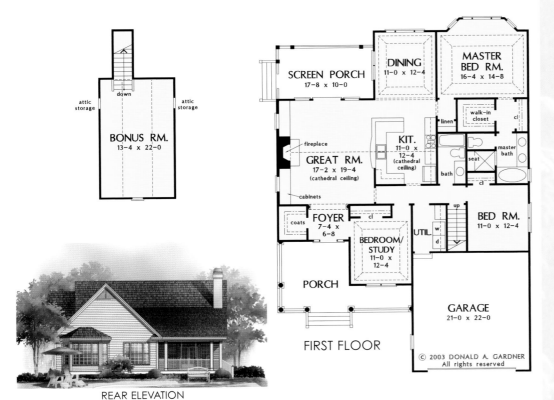

REAR ELEVATION

Woodbine

We finally built our cottage in the woods, and our daughter has told us how she envisions her bedroom with soft colors, flowers and lots of lace.

Plan ATSDG01-518E2

- Total Living: 1770 s.f.
- Bonus Room: 401 s.f.
- 3 Bedrooms, 2 Baths
- Width: 54'0"
- Depth: 57'8"
- Crawlspace Foundation
- Price Category B

FIRST FLOOR

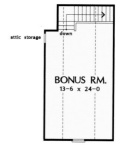

REAR ELEVATION

1-800-388-7580
www.allthingssouthern.com

© 2004 Donald A. Gardner, Inc.

*M*y son's an artist, and my grandson loves tractors. When they built their bungalow, my son painted a large antique tractor on my grandson's bedroom wall.

Cheraw

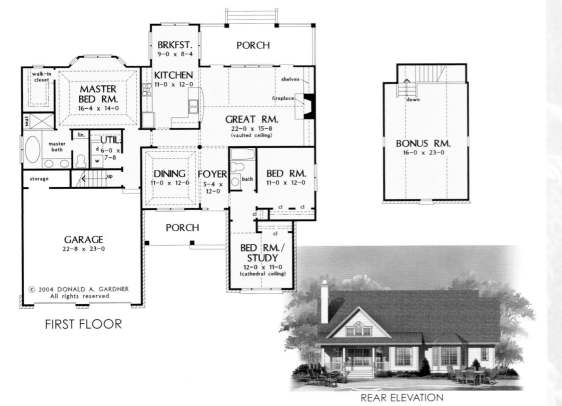

FIRST FLOOR

BRKFST.
9-0 x 8-4

PORCH

KITCHEN
11-0 x 12-0

walk-in closet

MASTER BED RM.
16-4 x 14-0

shelves

fireplace

master bath

lin.

UTIL
d 6-0 x
w 7-8

GREAT RM.
22-0 x 15-8
(vaulted ceiling)

storage

DINING
11-0 x 12-0

FOYER
5-4 x
12-0

bath

BED RM.
11-0 x 12-0

up

GARAGE
22-8 x 23-0

PORCH

cl cl

cl

cl

BED RM./
STUDY
12-0 x 11-0
(cathedral ceiling)

BONUS RM.
16-0 x 23-0

down

REAR ELEVATION

Plan ATSDG01-1060

- Total Living: 1795 s.f.
- Bonus Room: 444 s.f.
- 3 Bedrooms, 2 1/2 Baths
- Width: 57'6"
- Depth: 56'6"
- Crawlspace Foundation
- Price Category B

lay my burdens down

Donald A. Gardner Architects, Inc.

Liberty Hill

We collect county fair memorabilia, so after we converted the bonus rooms into bedrooms, one of them displays all of our whimsical county fair finds.

Plan ATSDG01-414

- Total Living: 1883 s.f.
- First Floor: 1803 s.f.
- Second Floor: 80 s.f.
- Bonus Room: 918 s.f.
- 3 Bedrooms, 2 Baths
- Width: 63'8"
- Depth: 57'4"
- Crawlspace Foundation
- Price Category B

FIRST FLOOR

SECOND FLOOR

REAR ELEVATION

*H*eirlooms are treasured in the South. My house is full of family antiques. My great, great, great grandmother's hope chest highlights my bedroom.

Unison Creek

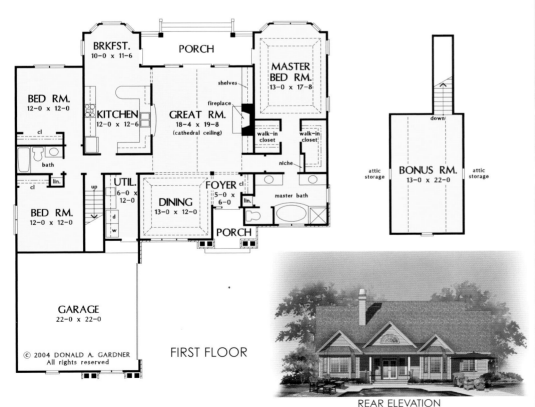

BRKFST.
10-0 x 11-6

PORCH

MASTER BED RM.
13-0 x 17-8

shelves

fireplace

BED RM.
12-0 x 12-0

KITCHEN
12-0 x 12-6

GREAT RM.
18-4 x 19-8
(cathedral ceiling)

walk-in closet

walk-in closet

niche

cl

bath

lin.

UTIL.
6-0 x 12-0

up

FOYER
5-0 x 6-0

cl

lin.

master bath

BED RM.
12-0 x 12-0

DINING
13-0 x 12-0

PORCH

d

w

GARAGE
22-0 x 22-0

FIRST FLOOR

down

attic storage

BONUS RM.
13-0 x 22-0

attic storage

REAR ELEVATION

Plan ATSDG01-1055

- Total Living: 1956 s.f.
- Bonus Room: 358 s.f.
- 3 Bedrooms, 2 Baths
- Width: 57'0"
- Depth: 66'8"
- Crawlspace Foundation
- Price Category B

© 1999 Donald A. Gardner, Inc.

Prynnwood

Plan ATSDG01-818

- Total Living: 2037 s.f.
- First Floor: 1502 s.f.
- Second Floor: 535 s.f.
- Bonus Room: 275 s.f.
- 3 Bedrooms, 2 1/2 Baths
- Width: 43'0"
- Depth: 57'6"
- Crawlspace Foundation
- Price Category C

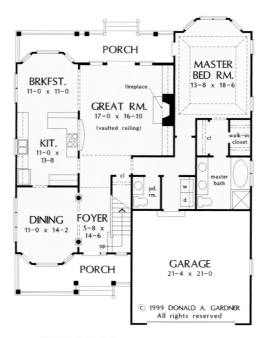

FIRST FLOOR

PORCH

BRKFST.
11-0 x 11-0

GREAT RM.
17-0 x 16-10
(vaulted ceiling)

fireplace

MASTER
BED RM.
13-8 x 18-6

KIT.
11-0 x
13-8

cl

walk-in
closet

cl

master
bath

DINING
11-0 x 14-2

FOYER
5-8 x
14-6

pd.
rm.

w

d

up

GARAGE
21-4 x 21-0

PORCH

SECOND FLOOR

great room below

cl cl

railing

down

lin.

cl cl

BED RM.
11-0 x 12-0

bath

BED RM.
11-0 x 13-6

foyer below

attic storage

BONUS RM.
12-8 x 18-6

attic storage

REAR ELEVATION

154

Q uilts teach us a lot about preserving history and finding new uses for old things. I'm most proud of my quilt collection and display it in my bedroom.

Orchard Park

Plan ATSDG01-703

- Total Living: 2042 s.f.
- Bonus Room: 475 s.f.
- 3 Bedrooms, 2 1/2 Baths
- Width: 75'11"
- Depth: 56'7"
- Crawlspace Foundation
- Price Category C

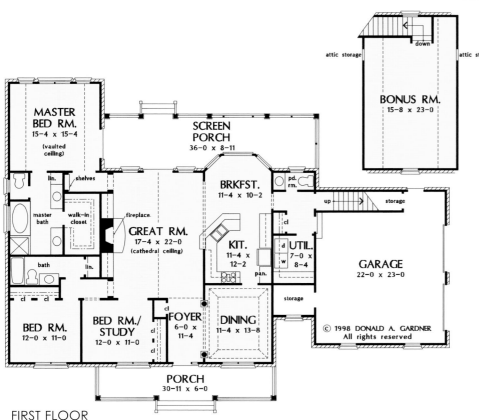

BONUS RM.
15-8 x 23-0

FIRST FLOOR

Ashby

We built a window seat in our master bedroom's bay window. I love to relax and look out to the beautiful weeping willow tree in the backyard.

Plan ATSDG01-1061

- Total Living: 2051 s.f.
- First Floor: 1502 s.f.
- Second Floor: 549 s.f.
- Bonus Room: 285 s.f.
- 3 Bedrooms, 3 1/2 Baths
- Width: 43'0"
- Depth: 57'6"
- Crawlspace Foundation
- Price Category C

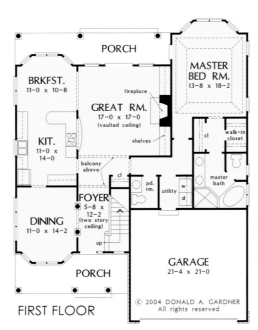

FIRST FLOOR

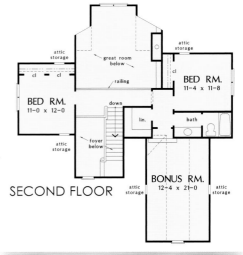

SECOND FLOOR

REAR ELEVATION

We wanted to capture the Lowcountry in our master bedroom, so we purchased a wrought-iron bed and fitted it with silk fabrics in deep hues of blue.

Erindale

Plan ATSDG01-510

- Total Living: 2057 s.f.
- Bonus Room: 444 s.f.
- 3 Bedrooms, 3 Baths
- Width: 80'10"
- Depth: 56'4"
- Crawlspace Foundation
- Price Category C

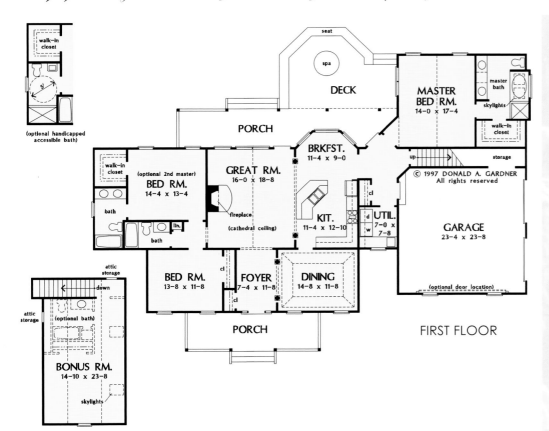

FIRST FLOOR

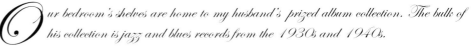

© 2001 Donald A. Gardner, Inc.

Meadowsweet

Our bedroom's shelves are home to my husband's prized album collection. The bulk of his collection is jazz and blues records from the 1930s and 1940s.

Plan ATSDG01-918

- Total Living: 2211 s.f.
- First Floor: 1476 s.f.
- Second Floor: 735 s.f.
- Bonus Room: 374 s.f.
- 4 Bedrooms, 2 1/2 Baths
- Width: 48'4"
- Depth: 51'4"
- Crawlspace Foundation
- Price Category C

SECOND FLOOR

FIRST FLOOR

REAR ELEVATION

*Our daughter loves horses and has been riding since she was a little girl.
We gave her the bedroom that overlooks the stables.*

SECOND FLOOR

BED RM.
12-0 x 11-8

BONUS RM.
13-2 x 18-0

BED RM.
12-0 x 11-0

attic storage

7-2 x 7-4

attic storage

great room below

foyer below

cl

bath

lin.

down

cl

FIRST FLOOR

MASTER BED RM.
16-0 x 13-0
(cathedral ceiling)

walk-in closet

master bath

seat

UTIL.
9-4 x 6-2

d w

BRKFST.
12-0 x 10-8

PORCH

KITCHEN
12-0 x 12-8

GREAT RM.
19-2 x 16-0
(vaulted ceiling)

fireplace

shelves

seat

bath

GARAGE
22-0 x 23-2

© 2003 DONALD A. GARDNER
All rights reserved

storage

pan.

sto.

K

DINING
12-0 x 13-4

FOYER
7-8 x 7-8

up

BED RM./ STUDY
11-4 x 12-4
(vaulted ceiling)

PORCH

Derbyville

Plan ATSDG01-1032

- Total Living: 2276 s.f.
- First Floor: 1778 s.f.
- Second Floor: 498 s.f.
- Bonus Room: 315 s.f.
- 4 Bedrooms, 3 Baths
- Width: 54'8"
- Depth: 53'2"
- Crawlspace Foundation
- Price Category C

REAR ELEVATION

lay my burdens down
Donald A. Gardner Architects, Inc.

Weatherford

The clematis vine has just reached the top of our bedroom window's ledge. I'm going to train it to grow around the bay.

Plan ATSDG01-1053

- Total Living: 2304 s.f.
- Bonus Room: 361 s.f.
- 4 Bedrooms, 3 Baths
- Width: 58'4"
- Depth: 69'8"
- Crawlspace Foundation
- Price Category C

FIRST FLOOR

MASTER BED RM. 14-0 x 18-8
walk-in closet
walk-in closet
fireplace
GREAT RM. 15-8 x 19-0
(cathedral ceiling) shelves
master bath
lin.
seat
bath
cl
BED RM./STUDY 14-0 x 13-4
FOYER 5-8 x 13-4
DINING 12-0 x 13-4
PORCH
PORCH
BRKFST. 11-4 x 10-4
pantry
KITCHEN 13-4 x 16-0
BED RM. 13-8 x 11-0
cl
bath
cl
BED RM. 11-4 x 12-0
w d
UTILITY 11-4 x 6-0
up
storage
GARAGE 22-8 x 23-0
storage

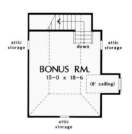

BONUS RM. 15-0 x 18-6 (8' ceiling)
attic storage
down
attic storage
attic storage

REAR ELEVATION

When the sunshine streams through the skylights, it looks as if there are windows open to the heavens, and it's the most pleasant alarm clock I've ever had.

Woodland

Plan ATSDG01-256

- Total Living: 2321 s.f.
- First Floor: 1756 s.f.
- Second Floor: 565 s.f.
- 4 Bedrooms, 3 Baths
- Width: 56'8"
- Depth: 42'4"
- Crawlspace Foundation
- Price Category C

FIRST FLOOR

SECOND FLOOR

REAR ELEVATION

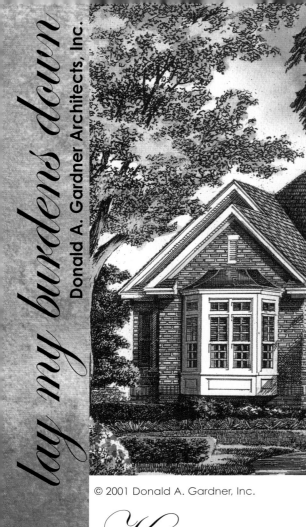

lay my burdens down
Donald A. Gardner Architects, Inc.

Kerwin

I've always wanted a sleeping porch, and the screen porch presented the perfect opportunity for my interpretation. It features an antique day bed.

Plan ATSDG01-913

- Total Living: 2461 s.f.
- Bonus Room: 397 s.f.
- 4 Bedrooms, 2 Baths
- Width: 71'2"
- Depth: 67'2"
- Crawlspace Foundation
- Price Category C

FIRST FLOOR

1-800-388-7580
www.allthingssouthern.com

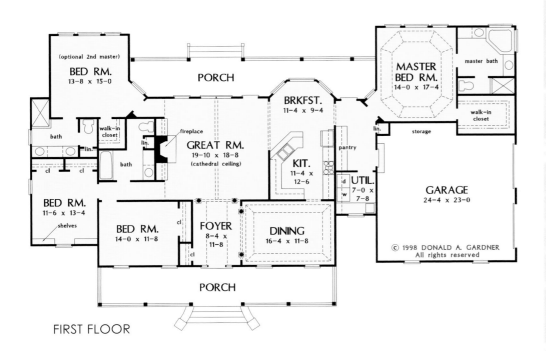

The South is known for tropical vegetation, so we incorporated large corn plants in our bedroom to remind us of our earlier years.

Peppergrass

Plan ATSDG01-733

- Total Living: 2487 s.f.
- 4 Bedrooms, 3 Baths
- Width: 86'2"
- Depth: 51'8"
- Crawlspace Foundation
- Price Category C

FIRST FLOOR

Cherryvale

My husband searched for an antique Audubon print of an animal indigenous to our state. He finally purchased one at auction, and it now resides in our bedroom.

Plan ATSDG01-533

- Total Living: 2511 s.f.
- First Floor: 1914 s.f.
- Second Floor: 597 s.f.
- Bonus Room: 487 s.f.
- 3 Bedrooms, 2 1/2 Baths
- Width: 79'2"
- Depth: 51'6"
- Crawlspace Foundation
- Price Category D

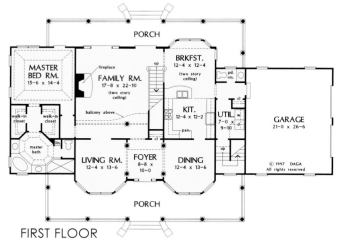

FIRST FLOOR

SECOND FLOOR

REAR ELEVATION

I come from a large family where my brother and I shared a room. I like to tease my wife about her being a better roommate. And the room smells so much better.

Sunnybrook

Plan ATSDG01-484

- Total Living: 2596 s.f.
- First Floor: 1939 s.f.
- Second Floor: 657 s.f.
- Bonus Room: 386 s.f.
- 4 Bedrooms, 3 Baths
- Width: 80'10"
- Depth: 55'8"
- Crawlspace Foundation
- Price Category D

FIRST FLOOR

BONUS RM.
21-0 x 19-3

REAR ELEVATION

SECOND FLOOR

Edgewater

Sweet tea and conversation are two things we love to share, so we covered and screened in the deck off the master bedroom for our outdoor haven.

Plan ATSDG01-1009

- Total Living: 2818 s.f.
- 4 Bedrooms, 3 Baths
- Width: 70'0"
- Depth: 69'10"
- Crawlspace Foundation
- Price Category D

FIRST FLOOR

REAR ELEVATION

*T*he kids love to run in and wake us up on Saturday mornings.
Our ritual involves everybody piling on our bed to watch our favorite program.

Cedar Creek

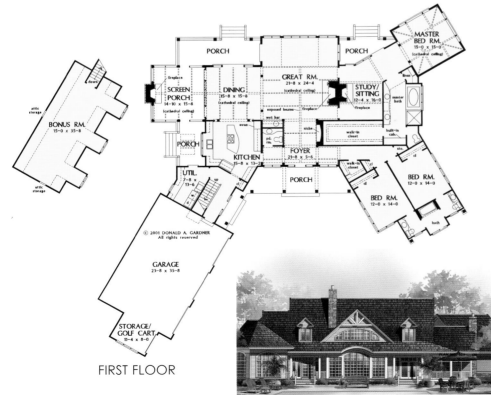

FIRST FLOOR

REAR ELEVATION

Plan ATSDG01-959

- Total Living: 3188 s.f.
- Bonus Room: 615 s.f.
- 3 Bedrooms, 2 1/2 Baths
- Width: 106'4"
- Depth: 104'1"
- Crawlspace Foundation
- Price Category E

lay my burdens down
Donald A. Gardner Architects, Inc.

Yesterview

*T*he first morning we woke in our new bedroom, I told my husband this house already felt like home. He sweetly replied, "Yes ma'am. It really does."

Plan ATSDG01-1002

- Total Living: 3419 s.f.
- First Floor: 2237 s.f.
- Second Floor: 1182 s.f.
- Bonus Room: 475 s.f.
- 4 Bedrooms, 3 1/2 Baths
- Width: 85'4"
- Depth: 56'4"
- Crawlspace Foundation
- Price Category E

FIRST FLOOR

PORCH

BRKFST.
12-0 x 12-4

GREAT RM.
19-0 x 20-0
(cathedral ceiling)

MASTER
BED RM.
19-2 x 14-0

fireplace

fireplace

KITCHEN
14-0 x 11-4

pantry

shelves

balcony above

GARAGE
22-0 x 31-0

walk-in
closet

niche

master
bath

(two story
ceiling)

FOYER
10-4 x 11-0

DINING
12-0 x 14-0

pd.
rm.

UTIL.
8-4 x
11-0

PORCH

SECOND FLOOR

BED RM.
14-2 x 17-8

great room
below

BED RM.
14-2 x 11-8

attic
storage

BONUS
13-4 x 31-0

attic
storage

railing

down
(8' ceiling)

lin.

walk-in
closet

bath

down

railing

foyer
below

BED RM.
12-8 x 12-4

bath

attic
storage

REAR ELEVATION

W e go to a lot of folk art fairs in this region. Our bedroom shelves are full of woven baskets, and our bathroom's full of old-time soaps and candles.

Wellingley

Plan ATSDG01-943

- Total Living: 3573 s.f.
- First Floor: 2511 s.f.
- Second Floor: 1062 s.f.
- Bonus Room: 465 s.f.
- 4 Bedrooms, 3 1/2 Baths
- Width: 84'11"
- Depth: 55'11"
- Crawlspace Foundation
- Price Category F

FIRST FLOOR

SECOND FLOOR

REAR ELEVATION

Index

FLOOR PLANS INDEX

Prints – What's in a Set?

Each set of Donald A. Gardner plans is a collection of drawings (including components such as floor plans, dimensions, cross sections and elevations) that show you exactly how your house is to be built. Most of our plan packages include:

COVER SHEET

An artist's rendering of the exterior of the house shows you approximately how the house will look when built and landscaped.

FOUNDATION PLAN

This sheet gives the foundation layout, including support walls, excavated and unexcavated areas, if any, and foundation notes. If the foundation is basement rather than monolithic slab, the plan shows footing and details.

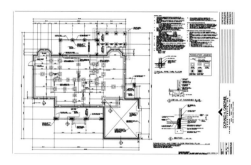

DETAILED FLOOR PLANS

These plans show the layout of each floor of the house. Rooms and interior spaces are carefully dimensioned and keys are given for cross-section details provided later in the plans, as well as window and door size callouts. These plans also show the location of kitchen appliances and bathroom fixtures, as well as suggested locations for electrical fixtures, switches and outlets.

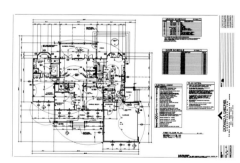

INTERIOR ELEVATIONS/ROOF PLAN

These drawings show the specific details and design of cabinets, utility rooms, fireplaces, bookcases, built-in units and other special interior features depending on the nature and complexity of the item. The roof plan shows the overall layout and necessary details for roof construction. If trusses are used, we suggest using a local truss manufacturer to design your trusses to comply with local codes and regulations.

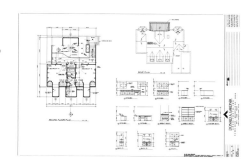

EXTERIOR ELEVATIONS/WALL SECTIONS

Included are front, rear, left and right sides of the house. Exterior materials, details and measurements are also given. This sheet also shows details of the house from the roof to the foundation. This section specifies the home's construction, insulation, flooring and roofing details.

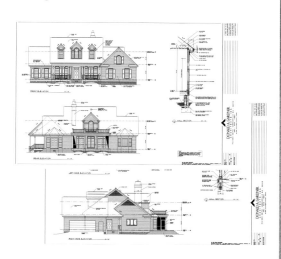

CROSS-SECTION DETAILS

Important changes in floor, ceiling and roof heights or the relationship of one level to another are called out. Also shown, when applicable, are exterior details such as railing and banding.

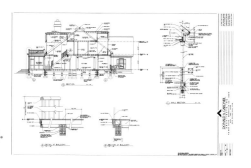

STRUCTURAL PLAN

This sheet gives the overall layout and necessary details for the ceiling, second floor framing (if applicable) and roof construction.

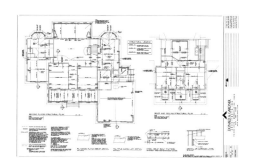

Before You Order

QUICK TURNAROUND

Because you are placing your order directly, we can ship plans to you quickly. If your order is placed Monday through Friday before 11 a.m. ET, we can usually have your plans to you the next business day. Some restrictions may apply. **We cannot ship to a post office box**; please provide a physical street address.

OUR EXCHANGE POLICY

Since our blueprints are printed especially for you at the time you place your order, we cannot accept any returns. If, for some reason, you find that the plan that you purchased does not meet your needs, then you may exchange that plan for another plan in our collection, but all exchanges must be pre-approved by the Customer Service department. We allow you 60 days from the time of purchase to make an exchange. All sets must be returned prior to the exchange taking place. At the time of the exchange, you will be charged a processing fee of 20 percent of the total amount of the original order plus the difference in price between the plans (if applicable) and the cost to ship the new plans to you. Vellums cannot be exchanged. All sets must be approved and authorization given before the exchange can take place. Please call our Customer Service department if you have any questions.

LOCAL BUILDING CODES AND ZONING REQUIREMENTS

Our plans are designed to meet or exceed national building standards. Because of the great differences in geography and climate, each state, county and municipality has its own building codes and zoning requirements. Your plan may need to be modified to comply with local requirements regarding snow loads, energy codes, soil and seismic conditions and a wide range of other matters. Prior to using plans ordered from us, we strongly advise that you consult a local building official.

ARCHITECTURE AND ENGINEERING SEALS

Some cities and states are now requiring that a licensed architect or engineer review and approve any set of building documents prior to construction. This is due to concerns over energy costs, safety, structural integrity and other factors. Prior to applying for a building permit or the start of actual construction, we strongly advise that you consult your local building official who can tell you if such a review is required.

DISCLAIMER

We have put substantial care and effort into the creation of our plans. We authorize the use of our plans on the express condition that you strictly comply with all local building codes, zoning requirements and other applicable laws, regulations and ordinances. However, because we cannot provide on-site consultation, supervision or control over actual construction, and because of the great variance in local building requirements, building practices and soil, seismic, weather and other conditions, WE CANNOT MAKE ANY WARRANTY, EXPRESS OR IMPLIED, WITH RESPECT TO THE CONTENT OR USE OF OUR PRINTS OR VELLUMS, INCLUDING BUT NOT LIMITED TO ANY WARRANTY OF MERCHANTABILITY OR OF FITNESS FOR A PARTICULAR PURPOSE. Please Note: Floor plans are not construction documents and are subject to change. Renderings are artists' concept only.

HOW MANY PRINTS WILL YOU NEED?

We offer a single set of prints so that you can study and plan your dream home in detail. However, you cannot build from this package. One set of blueprints is marked "NOT FOR CONSTRUCTION." If you are planning to get estimates from a contractor or subcontractor, or if you are planning to build immediately, you will need more sets. A single set or "study set" can be upgraded to a larger set package for a nominal fee.

Set packages are less expensive. Make sure you order enough to satisfy all your requirements. Sometimes changes are needed to a plan; in that case we offer vellums that are erasable and reproducible so changes can be made directly to the plans. Vellums are the only set that can be reproduced; it is illegal to copy prints. The following checklist will help determine how many sets you will need:

PLAN CHECKLIST

_____ **Owner (one set for notes, one for file)**

_____ **Builder (generally requires at least three sets; one as a legal document, one for inspections and at least one to give subcontractors)**

_____ **Local Building Department (often requires two sets)**

_____ **Mortgage Lender (usually one set for a conventional loan; three sets for FHA or VA loans)**

_____ **Total Number of Sets**

IGNORING COPYRIGHT LAWS CAN BE A
$1,000,000 Mistake!

Recent changes in the US copyright laws allow for statutory penalties of up to $150,000 per incident for copyright infringement involving any of the copyrighted plans found in this publication. The law can be confusing. So, for your own protection, take the time to understand what you cannot do when it comes to home plans.

What You Can't Do!
- **You Cannot Duplicate Home Plans.**
- **You Cannot Copy Any Part Of A Home Plan To Create Another.**
- **You Cannot Build A Home Without Buying A Blueprint Or License.**
- **You Cannot Build A Home From A Study Set. Study Sets Do Not Include Licenses.**

How To Order

Donald A. Gardner Architects, Inc.
150 Executive Center Drive, Ste. 215
Greenville, SC 29615
1-800-388-7580
www.allthingssouthern.com

Additional Items
Blueprints (per set)..$ 60.00
Full Reverse Blueprints.....................................$125.00

Materials List
Plan Categories A - E ....$ 65.00
Plan Category F - L..$ 75.00

Basement Plans
Plan Categories A - C $225.00
Plan Categories D - E $250.00
Plan Category F - L..$275.00

11" x 17" Color Front Perspective Rendering* $100.00
Specification Outline* ....$ 15.00
*Call for availability

Shipping & Handling
Overnight ....$ 40.00
Priority Overnight ....$ 50.00
2nd Day..$ 32.00
Ground ....$ 20.00
Saturday (If available) ....$ 50.00
International Delivery (Please call for prices & availability).

PLAN PRICE SCHEDULE

	1 Study Set	4 Sets	8 Sets	Vellum
A	$525	$575	$635	$795
B	$570	$620	$680	$860
C	$615	$665	$725	$925
D	$660	$710	$770	$990
E	$705	$755	$815	$1055
F	$775	$825	$885	$1135
G	$850	$900	$960	$1215
H	$950	$1000	$1060	$1315
I	$1050	$1100	$1160	$1415
J	$1150	$1200	$1260	$1515

Prices subject to change without notice.

Order Form

Plan Number _____

☐ 1-set (study only) . . . .$_____
☐ 4-set building package . . . .$_____
☐ 8-set building package . . . .$_____
☐ 1-set of reproducible vellums . . . .$_____

___ Additional Identical Plans @ $60 each $_____
___ Full Reverse Plans @ $125 each $_____
___ Basement Plans (See pricing above) $_____

Sub-Total $_____
Shipping and Handling $_____
Sales Tax (SC Res.) 5% $_____

Total $_____

Check one: ☐Visa ☐MasterCard ☐AmEx ☐Discover
Credit Card Number _____
Expiration Date _____
Signature _____

Name _____
Company _____
Street _____
City _____ State____ Zip _____
Daytime Telephone Number (_____) _____
Check one:
☐Consumer ☐Builder ☐Developer

We would like to give special thanks to:

Matthew Scott of Matthew Scott Photographer, Inc.; Walter Kirk III of Windward Photography; John Riley of Riley & Riley Photography, Inc.; and Stephen Stinson of Stephen Stinson Photography for their talent and creativity.

Greg Havens; Barry Nathan; and Rob Dent of Architectural Art for their beautiful illustrations.

DMG Atlanta for their pre-press expertise.

Toppan Printing for their hard work and dedication to this book.

The entire family of Donald A. Gardner employees for their hands-on and behind-the-scenes contributions that made this book possible.

And finally, a very special thanks to the homeowners for opening their homes to us.